# THE READER'S THEATRE OF
# AMERICAN PLAYS

### ADAPTED BY HENRY GILFOND

## TABLE OF C[...]

ISBN 0-89187-476-3
Curriculum Associates, Inc.
5 Esquire Road, North Billerica, MA 01862-2589

Reprinted by arrangement with Walker and Company

# THE ADVENTURE OF THE GERMAN STUDENT

## from the story by Washington Irving

*This is a story about dreams and evil spirits. We may not take evil spirits very seriously, but they are very real to Wolfgang, the young German student. He has been working very hard at his studies. He has been very tense. Most of all, he has been very nervous about the "evil spirits" that he believes follow him. He meets a beautiful young lady, the lady of his dreams. Will she be able to save him from the "evil spirits"? Or is she herself just another "evil spirit" in disguise?*

*Prepare yourself. This is an eerie story.*

THE CAST     *Announcer*
*Wolfgang*, the German student
*Franz*
*Peter*
*Hans*
*Jean*
*Claire*
*First Policeman*
*Second Policeman*

THE SETS     A student's room in Germany
A street in Paris
Wolfgang's room in Paris

THE ADVENTURE OF THE GERMAN STUDENT is an adaptation by Henry Gilfond of the short story of the same title by Washington Irving.
This adaptation ©1966 by Henry Gilfond

**4** *The Adventure of the German Student*

| | |
|---|---|
| Announcer | This story took place almost two hundred years ago. It might, however, have happened today. Though we laugh at ghosts and evil spirits, sometimes we cannot help thinking that we just might be wrong. Then a cold and clammy sensation runs up and down our spines. This story takes place in Germany and France; it might just as well take place right here, in the United States. |
| Wolfgang | (Strongly) No, I have never seen it! But I have felt it! I have felt its fingers on my throat and its breath on my mouth! I know it is here! |
| Franz | You've been studying too much, Wolfgang. You've been working too hard. |
| Wolfgang | (Laughs) You think I've gone mad! It's all in my imagination! All in my dreams! |
| Peter | There are no evil spirits, Wolfgang. You know that as well as the rest of us. |
| Wolfgang | Then explain this thing! It comes in my dreams! It comes to me when I stand at this window and look out into the streets! |
| Hans | Does it come to you now, Wolfgang? |
| Wolfgang | No. It comes to me when I'm alone. Sometimes it comes as the face of a beautiful woman. |
| Franz | I thought you said that you never saw it! |

| | |
|---|---|
| *Wolfgang* | She is not the evil spirit! She is something else, something lovely. It's the evil spirit I can't see! And it's the evil spirit that wants to take hold of me, possess me, destroy me! |
| *Peter* | You need a rest, Wolfgang. |
| *Hans* | Why don't you take a vacation, Wolfgang? Take a rest from all these books. |
| *Franz* | We all need a vacation some time, Wolfgang. Why don't you go off somewhere for a while? Why don't you take a trip to Paris? There's a gay place for you. Forget all this evil spirit nonsense. |
| *Wolfgang* | I don't need a vacation. And I know what you're thinking, my good friends. You think I've gone mad. You're kind and you won't say what you're thinking. You think I really ought to be sent to some mental institution, but you won't say it! |
| *Hans* | We say what we mean, Wolfgang. You are nervous. You need a vacation. |
| *Wolfgang* | You think I can get away from the evil spirit. You are mistaken. It will follow me even if I go to Paris, or London, or anywhere else you send me. |
| *Franz* | We're not talking about the evil spirit, Wolfgang. We're just asking you to get away from your books and your studies for a while. I would go to Paris myself if I could afford it. |

| | |
|---|---|
| Wolfgang | And I can afford it? Suppose I do want to go to Paris, where am I going to get the money? |
| Peter | We'll lend you the money. |
| Hans | And you don't need to hurry to pay it back. |
| Wolfgang | The evil spirit will still be with me. It won't help. |
| Franz | You've got to go, Wolfgang, or it will really drive you mad. |
| Wolfgang | Yes, maybe I should go. *(He laughs.)* Perhaps the lovely young woman and her beautiful face will follow me there. Perhaps the evil one will lose its way on the journey. |
| Announcer | Wolfgang went to Paris, but he could not change his habits. He read and studied. The woman's beautiful face still came to his dreams, and he still could not rid himself of the evil spirit. |
| | Paris was in the midst of its revolution, at that time, and every day men and women were carried off to the guillotine, the machine that cut off a man's head. This was the French system for executing those who were thought to oppose the revolution. |
| | It is late. The night is stormy. Wolfgang walks the street with a new friend. |
| Wolfgang | She has come to me almost every night now. |

*The Adventure of the German Student* **7**

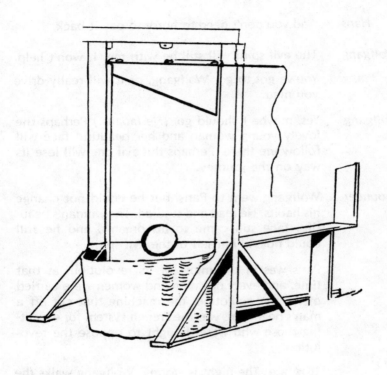

| Jean | This beautiful lady? |
|------|------|
| Wolfgang | You don't believe it? |
| Jean | Why, of course! We all dream of beautiful ladies, Wolfgang, my friend. |
| Wolfgang | But you don't believe that the evil spirit has followed me to Paris? |
| Jean | No. I cannot believe there are evil spirits, or spirits of any kind. |
| Wolfgang | Then you cannot understand the tortures I have suffered! It is always near me! It wants to swallow me! |
| Jean | You're mad, Wolfgang! |
| Wolfgang | At last some one has said it! I am mad, am I? |
| Jean | Yes, if you speak of some evil spirit that wants to swallow you. |
| Wolfgang | It is there, I tell you! And I am not mad! Though, it is a wonder that it hasn't driven me mad yet. Hush! What's that? I thought I heard a cry. |
| Jean | It's the guillotine. We are standing opposite the guillotine. Do you think you hear the ghosts crying? |
| Wolfgang | It's not a ghost. It's something alive. |

| | |
|---|---|
| *Jean* | It's nothing alive. The guillotine takes care of that. Death to all the enemies of France! |
| *Wolfgang* | I hear it. I hear it sobbing. |
| *Jean* | You are really mad, my friend. Go. Examine the guillotine, if you wish. Maybe you'll find that evil spirit you're always talking about. As for me, I'm going home. Good night, my friend. *(He leaves.)* |
| *Wolfgang* | A voice. I'm sure I heard a voice. *(As he moves to the guillotine)* Or am I really going mad? *(As he sees Claire, seated at the foot of the guillotine)* No! |

*(Claire, her face hidden in her lap, sobs aloud.)*

| | |
|---|---|
| *Wolfgang* | Ah, miss, you have lost some one. You have lost some one dear to you. |

*(Claire sobs)*

| | |
|---|---|
| *Wolfgang* | I am sorry. The guillotine is a dreadful instrument. I am sorry. I know that there is no comfort when you lose someone near to you, but I would like to help, miss. *(As Claire looks up at him)* Good God! We have met before! |
| *Claire* | Have we met? |
| *Wolfgang* | You have come to me so often! You have come to me night after night! You are the beautiful lady who has come to me in my dreams! |

| | |
|---|---|
| *Claire* | Ah! How kind of you. You want to comfort me. |
| *Wolfgang* | How wonderful to see you. Come! Let me take you out of this storm. |
| *Claire* | Where will you take me? |
| *Wolfgang* | Anywhere! Away from the wind and the thunder and lightning. I will take you to your friends. |
| *Claire* | I have no friends on earth. |
| *Wolfgang* | No friends? *(He laughs.)* Such beauty must have many friends! |
| *Claire* | I have no friends on earth. |
| *Wolfgang* | But I am your friend, beautiful lady. I will take you home. |
| *Claire* | My home is in the grave. That is where my home is, in the grave! |
| *Wolfgang* | Ah, you have suffered too much! It is so hard to lose one's dear ones. Come to my home. |
| *Claire* | My home is in the grave. |
| *Wolfgang* | Please don't say that again. I know you have suffered, but you may have my home. You have been there in my dreams so often, it might as well be yours. |

*The Adventure of the German Student* **11**

| | |
|---|---|
| *Claire* | My home... |
| *Wolfgang* | Please, beautiful lady! It's just a room. I'm a student, and a stranger here, but the room is yours; and I promise you, no harm will come to you. |
| *Claire* | You are kind. I begin to think that I, too, have seen your face before. |
| *Wolfgang* | Then you will come with me? |
| *Claire* | I will go with you. |
| *Announcer* | They walked together through the rainstorm, and for the first time in many months Wolfgang was really happy. He forgot about the evil spirit. He brought Claire into his room and there, with the full light on Claire's face, he became happier than he had ever been in all his life, for Claire was even more beautiful than he had ever dreamed. |
| *Wolfgang* | Your eyes! Your hair! Your mouth! I told you that you have come to me in my dreams night after night, but never so beautiful as you are now! Do you believe that you came to me in my dreams? |
| *Claire* | I came to you in your dreams. |
| *Wolfgang* | How happy you make me! I love you, my beautiful lady. I have loved you from the first time you came to me. Tell me why you came. I know, but you must tell me with your own lips. |

*The Adventure of the German Student* **13**

| | |
|---|---|
| *Claire* | Do I tell you with my eyes? |
| *Wolfgang* | Yes. But I want to hear it from your lips. |
| *Claire* | If my eyes tell you, that should be enough. |
| *Wolfgang* | It is enough. But say it once! I long to hear it from your lips. |
| *Claire* | You are kind. You are gentle. You are wild. |
| *Wolfgang* | Wild? I love you, my beautiful lady, and I want to hear you say *(quietly)* that you love....me. |
| *Claire* | How shall I say it? |
| *Wolfgang* | Say it simply. |
| *Claire* | I love you. |
| *Wolfgang* | Ah, I am in heaven! No more evil spirits! I have conquered them! Only the beautiful lady of my dreams! *(Calming down just a little)* We will get married in the morning! I am yours forever! |
| *Claire* | *(Very quietly)* Forever? |
| *Wolfgang* | Forever and ever. |
| *Claire* | Then I am yours. |
| | *(They embrace.)* |

| | |
|---|---|
| *Wolfgang* | *(Suddenly horrified, feeling Claire cold in his arms)* Darling! You are cold! Wake up! Wake up! *(Shrieking)* You are dead! Dead. |
| *Announcer* | The whole house woke up to Wolfgang's frantic shrieking. Soon there were policemen in his room. |
| *First Policeman* | *(Looking at Claire)* For heaven's sake, how did this woman get here? |
| *Wolfgang* | I brought her here. We were to get married in the morning. |
| *Second Policeman* | Married? To a corpse? |
| *Wolfgang* | Oh, beautiful lady! |
| *First Policeman* | You'd better calm yourself, young man. You'll have some explaining to do. |
| *Wolfgang* | She died in my arms! |
| *Second Policeman* | She died at the guillotine, young man. She was guillotined yesterday! |
| *Wolfgang* | *(Screams)* No! Who is mad now? She died in my arms, I tell you! |

| | |
|---|---|
| *First Policeman* | She did? |
| *Announcer* | The policeman stepped up to the body of the young, beautiful lady, untied the black collar around her neck, and the beautiful head rolled to the floor! |
| *Wolfgang* | *(Going completely mad)* Evil! The evil spirits have taken me! |
| *Second Policeman* | Calm, man. Calm. |
| *Wolfgang* | Can't you see? The evil spirits walked into her body! They trapped me! They will consume me! They will eat me up! *(Completely mad)* Go away! Go away! Go away, you evil spirits! Go away! |
| *Announcer* | This is how it was. The teller of this story says that it is entirely true. And he says that he himself has seen Wolfgang...in a hospital for people who have completely lost their minds. |

**16**  *The Adventure of the German Student*

# THE AMBITIOUS GUEST

## from the story by Nathaniel Hawthorne

*A young man enters an inn one cold, stormy night, and he is full of dreams and ambitions. The inn is built at the foot of a mountain which for many years has threatened to come down, burying the inn and all the people who live in it. Will the mountain come down this night? Will it bring an end to all the hopes of the eager young guest? Or will he leave the inn in the morning, free to pursue his ambitions?*

*Nathaniel Hawthorne wrote of simple people. But even in the simplest lives he discovered mystery, the mystery of man himself, and the even more mysterious ways of God with man. This is a story that is rich in suspense and full of wonder.*

THE CAST
*Father*, the owner of the inn
*Mother*, his wife, Esther
*Sarah*, their daughter
*Grandmother*
*First Child*, another of the children
*Second Child*, another of the children
*Young Man*, the visitor at the inn
*First Neighbor*
*Second Neighbor*
*Announcer*

THE SETS
The inn
Just outside the inn

THE AMBITIOUS GUEST is an adaptation by Henry Gilfond of the short story of the same title by Nathaniel Hawthorne. This adaptation ©1966 by Henry Gilfond

17

**Announcer**    There are many inns in the White Mountains of New England for the travelers who are journeying north to Vermont or south to Connecticut. But we are inside a special one of them — an inn built just under a huge mountain that seems always about to come down and bury it. As the play opens, the family that runs the inn does not seem to be aware of danger. In fact, the family is a very happy one. Outside, it is very cold and the wind is howling; but there is a huge fire warming the inn, and the family is at peace.

**Father**    There won't be many people out on a night like this.

**Sarah**    You never can tell, Father.

**Mother**    (Teasing her daughter) There is sure to be some handsome young man on the road, isn't there?

**Grandmother**    (To Sarah) You wouldn't mind opening the door for him, would you, Sarah?

**Sarah**    (Defiantly) No, I wouldn't!

**Father**    (To Sarah) It does get lonesome for you every now and then, doesn't it, Sarah?

**Sarah**    It never gets lonesome, Father. People always knock at our door. There's always some traveler who visits with us. Besides, we do have each other.

**Grandmother**    God be praised for that!

**First Child**    It's too cold for traveling tonight. No one will come.

| | |
|---|---|
| Second Child | Listen to that wind blow! It'll blow that mountain right down on top of us! |
| Father | Not tonight, Peter. |
| Second Child | Why not, Father? People are always saying that the mountain is going to come down some time. |
| First Child | Will it come down, Father? |
| Father | Perhaps. Some time. But not while we're here. I wouldn't have built the inn here if I had expected the mountain to fall down on us, would I? |
| First Child | Still, people do say that it will bury us all. |
| Mother | Nonsense. Now you had better go to bed and forget about it all. |
| Announcer | There is a sharp blast of wind and a rumble from the mountain. The house is very still for a moment. |
| Second Child | What was that, Mother? |
| Mother | The wind. The mountain talking. |
| First Child | I don't like the way it talks. |
| Father | It has been talking that way for a long time. Just go to bed, as your mother says, and have pleasant dreams. |
| Announcer | Suddenly the door rattles sharply. Again there is a stillness in the inn. |
| Grandmother | (To the children) It's just the wind. |

| | |
|---|---|
| *Announcer* | The door rattles again. It opens. A young man enters. For a moment no one says anything. |
| *Young Man* | Am I intruding? |
| *Father* | No, no, no! Come right in! Shut the door! It's cold out there! |
| *Young Man* | This is an inn, isn't it? |
| *Father* | Yes, it's an inn! And you're welcome! |
| *Young Man* | It's cold on the road. The wind is fierce. It's good to see a fire. |
| *Grandmother* | Come in and warm yourself, young man. Would you like something hot to drink? |
| *Young Man* | I wouldn't mind, thank you. |
| *Mother* | (*To Sarah*) Fix the young man something warm to drink, Sarah. |
| *Young Man* | Thank you. The wind is blowing the snow right off the tops of the mountains and into the road. |
| *First Child* | They say the wind will blow the whole mountain down. |
| *Second Child* | On top of us. Bury us. |
| *Grandmother* | Why don't you go to bed, children? |
| *Announcer* | There is another fierce blast of the wind, and a rumble comes from the mountain. |

**20** *The Ambitious Guest*

| | |
|---|---|
| *Father* | The old mountain lets us know that it's still there. Just so we don't forget him. |
| *Young Man* | You are not frightened by it? |
| *Father* | No! The mountain is an old, old neighbor of ours. We get along. Besides, if he really does get angry and come down on us, we have a good place where we can get away from him. |
| *Young Man* | You've built yourself a safe retreat? |
| *Father* | Well, we haven't exactly built it. It's there. We can move out of the house quickly if the mountain begins to slide, and we'll all be safe. There's no need to worry about it. |
| *Young Man* | *(Taking the hot drink that Sarah offers him)* Thank you. *(To the Father)* I shall not be worried, not with such a happy family around me. |
| *Sarah* | Are you on your way to Vermont? |
| *Young Man* | In the morning, God willing. And further than Vermont. |
| *Grandmother* | You are an ambitious young man. |
| *Young Man* | I want to do things, create things, leave a name in this world that people will remember. |
| *Sarah* | How? What do you want to do? What do you want to make? |

| | |
|---|---|
| Young Man | I'm not sure. But, if I were to die today, no one would know that I had lived at all. There would be no one interested in what I had accomplished in my short life. And the truth of the matter is that I have accomplished nothing. |
| Mother | Not everyone who is born lives to accomplish anything of great importance. There are some of us who are just happy to live out our lives in peace and contentment. |
| Young Man | Oh, but I am not one of those. |
| Announcer | There is another blast of wind, another rumble in the mountain. |
| Young Man | Blow, wind! Shout, mountain! I am not ready to die! When I have done what I was born to do, then I will be ready to die! I will have built my monument! And I will be remembered! |
| Sarah | Such ambition frightens me. I would rather sit here at the fire, warm and comfortable. I don't think it matters very much whether the world knows about us. I think it is enough that we are here together and love each other. |
| Father | I'm not so sure about that, Sarah. It's natural for a young man to be ambitious. There are things that I might have done... Perhaps there are still things that I can accomplish in my lifetime. |
| Mother | Are you thinking of what you will do after I die? |

| | |
|---|---|
| Father | No! When I think of your death, Esther, I think of mine, too. I was just thinking that it might be pleasant to have a good farm. Somewhere near these White Mountains, but not under them, where they can tumble down on our heads. I should like to be buried in a graveyard with a stone at my head. |
| Young Man | There! Just as I said! We all want to leave a monument behind us! |
| Mother | I don't like this talk. They say it's a sign, when people's minds begin to wander this way. *(To the children)* It's long past your bedtime. |
| First Child | Let's all go down to the brook, Mother. |
| Second Child | Yes, Mother. Let's go drink the water out of the brook! |
| Mother | Nonsense, children. It's too cold out there. |
| Announcer | Outside the inn door, there is the rattle of a wagon and the sound of voices. |
| Sarah | They're calling your name, Father. |
| Father | You're imagining it. It's just some people on the road. |
| Sarah | I heard them, Father. They were calling you. |
| Father | They'll come in if they want to. The inn is open, Sarah. |
| Sarah | You should ask them in, Father. Perhaps they have a message for you. |
| Announcer | The noise from the mountain sounds again. |

## 24  The Ambitious Guest

| | |
|---|---|
| *Grandmother* | Don't be frightened, Sarah. |
| *Sarah* | I am not frightened, Grandmother, but I think we ought to open the door. I think we ought to see who was calling Father. |
| *Father* | No one was calling me, Sarah. |
| *Announcer* | They hear the wagon rolling away from the inn. |
| *First Child* | Now they've gone! They could have given us a ride to the brook! |
| *Young Man* | Do you have many neighbors? |
| *Father* | Very few, but they are good neighbors. Always ready to help each other, especially if someone is ill or there is some other kind of trouble. |
| *Sarah* | They would warn us if they thought the mountain was going to fall down on us. |
| *Young Man* | Are you really worried? |
| *Sarah* | No. |
| *Young Man* | Then what are you thinking right now? |
| *Sarah* | Nothing, really. I felt just a little lonesome. Just for a moment. |
| *Young Man* | Do you know, I have a strange gift? I can always tell what another person is feeling, in his heart. |
| *Sarah* | Really? |
| *Young Man* | Really! Shall I tell you what you were really feeling? |

| | |
|---|---|
| *Sarah* | How can you? How can a young man tell how a young girl feels? They would be your feelings, not mine. |
| *Announcer* | There is a new blast of the wind, stronger and fiercer than ever before; and the noise from the mountain is greater and louder. |
| *First Child* | What was that? |
| *Second Child* | It's coming down! |
| *Mother* | Children! You must go to bed! |
| *First Child* | I've never heard the mountain sound like that before, Mother. |
| *Grandmother* | It will sound that way again. Just shut your ears to it. |
| *Sarah* | We shut our ears to so many things, Grandmother. |
| *Grandmother* | Yes. And your mouths make up for it. |
| *Sarah* | You've been listening to us all evening. |
| *Grandmother* | I've been listening to you wishing and planning and letting your heads run on, from one thing to another, and I've begun to wonder—what can I wish for? What can *I* plan for? |
| *Young Man* | Tell us, Grandmother. |
| *Grandmother* | Well now, you tell me. What should an old woman wish for, when she is just a step or two from the grave? |
| *Father* | Tell us, Mother. |

| | |
|---|---|
| Grandmother | I hope for a decent burial. I've prepared for it a long time. I have a nice linen shroud and a cap with a muslin ruff. When I was a girl they used to say that if everything wasn't just right, if there was anything not smooth with the shroud or the cap, the cold hand of the corpse would rise to straighten it out. |
| Sarah | Don't talk that way, Grandmother! It makes me cold! |
| Grandmother | Now, I just want one of you to hold a mirror over my face, when I am in my coffin. Who knows but that I might take a quick look at myself, to see whether everything is all right. |
| Young Man | It's the monument again. Young or old, everyone dreams of it. |
| Sarah | Not all of us. |
| Young Man | Yes, all. I sometimes wonder how a sailor feels when his ship is sinking. Does he think that he will be buried in the ocean without any mark to say that he had been here? It must be a dreadful, empty feeling. |
| Announcer | Suddenly there is a blast of wind mightier than any before. The mountain roars, louder than ever. The house shakes. |
| Mother | The slide! |
| Father | Quick, children! Quick! |
| Sarah | (To the Young Man) Get out of here! Fast! |

| | |
|---|---|
| *Young Man* | Come! Let me help you! |
| *First Child* | Grandmother! |
| *Grandmother* | I am coming. God help us! |
| *Father* | (*As all move out of the door, to the Young Man*) Follow us! It will be cold, but we'll be safe! |
| *Announcer* | As they left, the mountain came down and buried everything in its path, everything but the little inn. Just before the slide reached the house it divided into two streams, burying everything beyond the house, but leaving the house itself untouched. In the morning, the neighbors came to see whether the innkeeper and his family were safe. |
| *First Neighbor* | There is still smoke coming from the chimney. |
| *Second Neighbor* | It was cold. They had a fire going. |
| *First Neighbor* | I think they had just one visitor. |
| *Second Neighbor* | Yes. It was some ambitious young man. I spoke with him on the road. He talked of monuments. |
| *First Neighbor* | It's a pity. If they had stayed inside the inn they would have been alive today. But they didn't. The Lord knows where they are buried. |
| *Second Neighbor* | The ways of God are strange. Perhaps this is how He wished it. |

# THE FIDDLER

## from the story
## by
## Herman Melville

*Every boy and girl and man and woman dreams of success; we are all ambitious. We want greatness in our careers, and most of us want to become rich as well. How many stories have we read of young people going out into the world to seek fame and fortune? In such stories, fame and fortune have a distinct meaning—once they have been achieved, our hero or heroine lives happily ever after.*

*But do fame and fortune always bring happiness?*

*The word "fiddler" has two meanings. It means, as we all know, someone who plays the violin. It may also mean someone who just "fiddles around," does things just for the fun of doing them, with no other purpose in mind. In this story, the "fiddler" is a person with a rather unusual history, and he will affect the hero of this tale in a rather unusual way. This story's hero is, when the story opens, an ambitious young man. Then he meets the "fiddler". In a few minutes, you, too, will meet the "fiddler". Will he affect you, as he did our hero?*

| | |
|---|---|
| THE CAST | Helmstone |
| | Standard |
| | Hautboy |
| THE SET | A restaurant |

THE FIDDLER is an adaptation by Henry Gilfond of
the short story of the same title by Herman Melville.
This adaptation ©1966 by Henry Gilfond

(*Helmstone is sitting at a table in a restaurant. He is reading a newspaper, becoming more and more irritated with what he reads. He slams the newspaper down on the table, as Standard enters.*)

**Standard**   (*In a very good mood*) Helmstone! I thought I'd find you here!

**Helmstone**   (*In a very bad mood*) You've been looking for me? You want to congratulate me?

**Standard**   (*Still in a good mood*) Congratulate you? Of course! What's the good news?

**Helmstone**   (*Pointing to his newspaper*) You haven't seen it, then?

**Standard**   Seen it? You mean the circus? Of course, I've seen it. A tremendous performance! And what an amazing clown!

**Helmstone**   I wasn't talking about the circus! (*Again pointing to the newspaper*) Have you read the review?

**Standard**   You mean the review of your book? It wasn't bad, was it?

**Helmstone**   You didn't find it good enough to mention. It's a miserable review! A vicious review!

**Standard**   Come now, Helmstone. You're taking it much too seriously. After all, it's only one man's opinion.

**Helmstone**   How else shall I take it? He's ruined me! Destroyed me! One short paragraph, and everything I've worked for, everything I've hoped for, everything I've dreamed, my whole career — finished! He might as well have shot me.

| | |
|---|---|
| *Standard* | You're exaggerating, Helmstone. |
| *Helmstone* | Exaggerating! Who'll want to read Helmstone, after the paragraph in this newspaper? Who'll know the blood, the sweat and the tears I poured into this book? |
| *Standard* | I will, Helmstone. I know the work you put into your novel. I will read it. I look forward to reading it. |
| *Helmstone* | I wanted the world to read it! I wanted the world to know that it had a new novelist, and perhaps a great one. |
| *Standard* | And that would make you happy? If the whole world read it? You want the whole world to stand up and cheer your name. Is that it? |
| *Helmstone* | Isn't that what every man wants? You look puzzled, Standard. Isn't that why you spend all your hours painting portraits in your studio, painting land-scapes, seascapes? We all want it — applause, honors, fame. That's why we sweat at our work. That's why we hope and dream. You and I, Standard, and all men of genius. |
| *Standard* | Not I, Helmstone. That's not why I sweat at my pictures. And that's not what I dream. And you've called me a man of genius. |
| *Helmstone* | Then you've no ambition, Standard! |
| *Standard* | Not your ambition. |
| *Helmstone* | What other ambition is there? |

| | |
|---|---|
| *Standard* | A simpler ambition, Helmstone. I'm ambitious for happiness. Success and fortune and the cheers of the crowd may be the most worthy goals for a man's work, but they don't necessarily promise happiness. |
| *Helmstone* | Nonsense! |
| *Standard* | Maybe. But here comes Hautboy! We'll talk again about this business of ambition and success and happiness, but tell me, have you met Hautboy yet? You must! |
| *Helmstone* | Hautboy? |
| *Standard* | There he is, at the door. Hautboy! |
| *Helmstone* | I noticed him at the circus. Hautboy? Who is he? |
| *Standard* | An amazing person. So you were at the circus? A wonderful performance. *(As Hautboy enters)* Hautboy! Come and join us. |
| *Hautboy* | *(Shaking hands with Standard)* It's good to see you. |
| *Standard* | *(Introducing the men to each other)* My good friend Helmstone, my good friend Hautboy. |
| *Hautboy* | *(Very friendly)* It's good to meet you, Helmstone. |
| *Helmstone* | *(Very formal)* Hautboy. |
| *Standard* | My friend Helmstone is in a rather bad mood today. |
| *Hautboy* | *(To Helmstone, indicating the newspaper)* A bad review, eh? |

| | |
|---|---|
| *Helmstone* | A miserable review! |
| *Hautboy* | I shall read your book, anyway. And I shall enjoy it. |
| *Helmstone* | Thank you. Good or bad, it makes no difference to you. |
| *Hautboy* | There's nothing all bad and nothing all good. I enjoy reading, as I enjoy listening to music, or looking at a painting. Wherever there is some pleasure to be found, I look for it. Perhaps it is a weakness on my part. |
| *Standard* | It can't be a weakness, if it gives you pleasure. |
| *Hautboy* | True. And weakness, too, can sometimes be a source of happiness, I think. Perhaps I'm wrong again, but I'm talking only of myself and my own happiness. Excuse me! There's someone at the other table I must see for a moment. |
| *Standard* | (As Hautboy exits) Of course. (To Helmstone) Well? How do you like this new friend of mine? |
| *Helmstone* | A strange man, if he means what he says. Rather simple, isn't he? I would say he doesn't think too much, or worry too much. |
| *Standard* | He is always thinking, Helmstone, but you are right; he worries very little. His mind, and I should say his heart, too, is on what life has to offer him by way of pleasure; and there is much of that. |
| *Helmstone* | So it would seem. He laughed so hard at the clown in the circus, that his whole body shook. He sat only a few seats away from me. I couldn't help watching him — and, I must admit, envying him. I've never seen anyone enjoy anything so thoroughly. |

| | |
|---|---|
| *Standard* | Ah, there's no one who enjoys things so much as Hautboy — a novel, a painting, a clown — anything. |
| *Helmstone* | I can rather believe it. As a matter of fact, at the circus I almost wished that I were Hautboy and that I could give myself so easily to the simple pleasures. |
| *Standard* | You could. |
| *Helmstone* | No. He must be a wealthy man, this Hautboy. One must be a man with a mind completely free of worries to be as easy-going and as cheerful as Hautboy. The genius, the man with a great drive to create in words or pictures or music, cannot be so easy in his mind. |
| *Standard* | Then you don't think my friend Hautboy is a genius? |
| *Helmstone* | A genius? Look at him! Short, fat, comfortable! A genius is lean and hungry, Standard. |
| *Standard* | But suppose your genius starts to eat, Helmstone. He gets fat, and there goes his genius! |
| *Helmstone* | Never! A genius can't get rid of his lean and hungry look, nor of his genius; no more than a freckle-face can get rid of his freckles. No, your Hautboy is an ordinary man with ordinary tastes and ordinary desires. He won't try to do anything beyond his ability, and he has no ambition at all. But let him hear the applause of an audience just once, and this Hautboy of yours will be a different man. |
| *Standard* | It is interesting that you should speak of applause, talking of Hautboy. |

| | |
|---|---|
| Helmstone | He has never heard them. They have made no difference to him. He is happy enough just going along with the crowd. His job is not to be cheered, but to do the cheering. |
| Standard | Interesting. Incidentally, Helmstone, you do know of Master Betty, don't you? |
| Helmstone | Master Betty? Of course. Who doesn't? You're talking about the twelve-year-old boy, the great actor? |
| Standard | He isn't twelve any more. |
| Helmstone | Of course not. But there was a genius for you! Twelve years old and a great actor. Imagine that! A twelve-year-old boy who walked on the stage as if he had been born on it. Applause? Why, the police couldn't keep order in the crowd that went out to greet him, any time he dared to walk in the streets. And the theaters weren't big enough to seat the mobs of people who came to see this young boy play Hamlet. There was genius! What has become of Master Betty? |
| Hautboy | (Returning) Ah, excuse me, gentlemen. |
| Standard | Sit down, Hautboy! |
| Hautboy | Again I'm sorry. I must leave. (To Helmstone) But we'll talk again, and I must read your book. |
| Helmstone | You flatter me. |
| Hautboy | Ah, no. It is you who flatter me. You wrote a book for me to read. A man who offers me the wisdom of his writing, flatters me. He does more. He offers me the pleasure of a new experience. Thank you. |

| | |
|---|---|
| Helmstone | (Overwhelmed) Thank you. |
| Hautboy | Thank *you*. And now, if you'll excuse me... |
| Standard | Not yet, Hautboy. You said you were going to play your fiddle for me. |
| Hautboy | So I did. I'll be home in half an hour. Will you be there? However, I do think you might get weary of my fiddling. |
| Standard | Now you know that will never be. Is my friend Helmstone welcome, too? |
| Hautboy | (To Helmstone) I live only five minutes away from here. If you would like to hear my fiddle, you will be most welcome. |
| Helmstone | Thank you. I'll be there. |
| Hautboy | Good! In half an hour, then... (He exits.) |
| Helmstone | So he's a fiddler? That's where his genius lies. I suppose he gives fiddling lessons, too! |
| Standard | He does. But he's not just an ordinary fiddler. |
| Helmstone | I'll make my own decision, after I've heard him play. |
| Standard | But you have heard him. |
| Helmstone | When? Where? |
| Standard | Do you remember the night we walked past the museum? You were talking about your novel. You were having difficulty finding a proper ending for your story. |

| | |
|---|---|
| *Helmstone* | Yes! You were quite helpful, and I was grateful. |
| *Standard* | All I did was listen to you talk. |
| *Helmstone* | Good listeners are hard to find. Ah, now I remember! We stopped to hear someone play the violin. It was quite a remarkable violin. Don't tell me that was Hautboy! |
| *Standard* | But it was. |
| *Helmstone* | Hautboy? |
| *Standard* | I knocked at his door. I had to meet him. And I did. |
| *Helmstone* | And you never spoke of it! Why, I've never heard a fiddle played so richly, so magnificently. The man *is* a genius! Why haven't you told me? |
| *Standard* | How could I? You've been so wrapped up in your novel. You've been working so hard for your fame. We've pulled away from each other, Helmstone. You see, the applause and the cheers of the crowd no longer interest me. There are things which are more important, and I've discovered them. |
| *Helmstone* | Since you met Hautboy! |
| *Standard* | Since I met Hautboy. And his fiddle. |
| *Helmstone* | That's a poor trade, it seems to me. You give up the drive for fame and fortune, all for a fiddle. |
| *Standard* | The man and the fiddle, Helmstone. They go together. |

| | |
|---|---|
| *Helmstone* | *(Looks at his newspaper)* Perhaps it isn't such a poor trade. Who is he, Standard? Who is this Hautboy? |
| *Standard* | You've met the man. You've seen him. You spoke with him. What else is there to say? |
| *Helmstone* | There is more. There's some mystery here, and you're keeping it from me. Who is he, Standard? |
| *Standard* | He's a genius, Helmstone. |
| *Helmstone* | I'm convinced of that. Tell me more. I want the details. |
| *Standard* | I don't know whether you'll believe the rest. |
| *Helmstone* | Speak, and I'll tell you whether I believe. |
| *Standard* | Very well. When he was a boy, only a boy, he tasted all the wines of glory. Wherever he went, the people flocked to see him, shouted his name, sang his praises, filled the biggest theaters in the biggest cities just to say they had seen him, and heard him. He was loved. He was worshipped. And he was only a boy. |
| *Helmstone* | Go on. |
| *Standard* | He had more honors heaped on him than he could carry — and more money than he could count. |
| *Helmstone* | And now? |
| *Standard* | Now he goes from house to house, teaching the fiddle to make his living. No one knows who he is, no one shouts his name; and only his friends, who hear him play his fiddle, applaud him. |

| | |
|---|---|
| *Helmstone* | And this is enough for him? He is happy? |
| *Standard* | You saw for yourself. |
| *Helmstone* | But a man of genius wants the applause of the crowd — needs it! |
| *Standard* | He had it, and he deliberately threw it away. It blocked the road to the happiness he wanted. He tossed away the cheers and the honors and the fame, but he kept his genius. As you said, he is perfectly happy. Do you understand, Helmstone? |
| *Helmstone* | I begin to. But his name? What is his real name, Standard. |
| *Standard* | I'll whisper it to you. *(He whispers in Helmstone's ear.)* |
| *Helmstone* | No! I've cheered him myself. I've waited in line half the night and shouted myself hoarse when he appeared on the stage! |
| *Standard* | *(Changing his tone)* So you got a nasty little review in the newspapers, Helmstone? |
| *Helmstone* | Forget it! You'll talk to me no more about news-paper reviews, about fame and fortune! *(Beginning to exit)* I'll meet you at Hautboy's! |
| *Standard* | Where are you going? |
| *Helmstone* | There are some papers at home, some pages of a new novel I was beginning to write. I want to tear them up! |
| *Standard* | Don't be too hasty, Helmstone! Are you sure you know what you are doing? |
| *Helmstone* | I've never been more sure of anything in my life! Tell me, Standard, where can I buy myself a fiddle? I want Hautboy to teach me! |

# THE GLORIOUS WHITEWASHER

## from the story by Mark Twain

*Tom Sawyer has a job to do. His Aunt Polly has ordered him to whitewash the fence in front of their house, but Tom would much rather be at the well, having fun with the boys and girls there, or maybe off swimming. Tom goes to work, but not for long. A little thinking, a bit of scheming, and some psychology, and Tom turns his unpleasant chore into a profit-making enterprise. It takes a mastermind to get other people to do your work for you and pay you for the "privilege."*

| | |
|---|---|
| THE CAST | *Announcer* |
| | *Tom Sawyer* |
| | *Aunt Polly* |
| | *Jim* |
| | *Ben Rogers* |
| | *Billy Fisher* |
| | |
| THE SET | The fence in front of Aunt Polly's house |

THE GLORIOUS WHITEWASHER is adapted by Henry Gilfond from *The Adventures of Tom Sawyer* by Mark Twain (Samuel L. Clemens). This adaptation © 1966 by Henry Gilfond

| Announcer | It was Saturday morning, and all the world was bright with summer. There was a song in every heart and music on everyone's lips. It was almost as if no one had a care in the world; no one, that is, except Tom Sawyer. Tom was coming out of his house with a big bucket of whitewash in one hand, a brush in the other, and Aunt Polly right behind him. |
|---|---|
| Tom | Do I have to do it, Aunt Polly? |
| Aunt Polly | The fence needs whitewashing, Tom Sawyer, and today is the day. See to it that you do a good job. |
| Tom | I can do it next Saturday, Aunt Polly. |
| Aunt Polly | You'll do it today, Tom Sawyer. |
| Tom | But it's such a big fence.... It's nearly a mile long. |
| Aunt Polly | The sooner you start, the sooner you'll have it done. |
| Tom | I thought I'd go fishing and bring home some fresh fish for dinner. |
| Aunt Polly | After you finish whitewashing the fence. |
| Tom | That will be never. I mean, there'll be no time for fishing if I have to finish the fence first. |
| Aunt Polly | Tom Sawyer! |
| Tom | All right, Aunt Polly. I'll do the fence. But there won't be any fish tonight. |

| | |
|---|---|
| Aunt Polly | You won't go hungry. Just you do your job, and don't you come back into the house until that fence is all clean and white! *(She exits.)* |
| Tom | *(To himself)* Why do I always have to do these jobs? Who wants to whitewash this fence? Who needs it? *(He dips his brush into the bucket of whitewash, smears the top of the fence.)* This is going to take all year. *(He stops as he hears Jim singing "Buffalo Gals.")* |
| Jim | *(Entering, with an empty bucket in his hands)* *(Singing)* Buffalo gals, won't you come out tonight, won't you come out tonight, won't you come out tonight? Buffalo gals, won't you.... *(He stops in front of the fence.)* What are you doing, Tom? |
| Tom | What do you think I'm doing? |
| Jim | Whitewashing the fence. Aunt Polly make you? |
| Tom | Do you want to try it? |
| Jim | Whitewash the fence? Nah! I'm going down to the well, get some water. |
| Tom | I'll get the water for you. |
| Jim | Nah! All the boys and girls are down at the well. It's fun fetching the water. |
| Tom | It won't hurt you, if you give the fence a couple of licks. |

**Jim**    Nah! I was told to get the water and not to stop and fool around with anybody.

**Tom**    Whitewashing isn't fooling around. Let me get your water.

**Jim**    Nah! Aunt Polly won't like it. She told me you'd ask me to help whitewash, told me to mind my own business.

**Tom**    You never mind Aunt Polly. That's the way she always talks. Give me the bucket!

**Jim**    *(Pulling the bucket away)* And have Aunt Polly give me a licking?

**Tom**    Aunt Polly never licks anybody. She'll whack you over the head with her thimble, but that never hurt anybody. *(Reaching for the bucket)* Come on, Jim. I'll give you a marble.

**Jim**    What kind of marble?

**Tom**    *(Pulling a marble from his pocket)* This one! A white one! Isn't it a beauty?

**Jim**    It's a beauty, all right. But, nah! I'm afraid of Aunt Polly.

**Tom**    She talks awful, but she never hurts anyone. Let me get the water for you, Jim, and I'll show you my sore toe.

**Jim**    And give me the marble, too?

**Tom**    Sure! Do you want to see my sore toe?

*The Glorious Whitewasher*

| | |
|---|---|
| Jim | Let me see it. |
| Tom | Sure. *(He begins to take off his shoe.)* And don't you worry about Aunt Polly. |
| Jim | *(As Aunt Polly enters, and he runs off with the pail)* Aunt Polly, Tom! Aunt Polly! |
| Aunt Polly | *(Whacking Tom with her slipper)* Tom Sawyer! Are you ever going to do anything the way I tell you to do it? |
| Tom | *(Protecting himself as well as he can)* I was just showing Jim my sore toe, Aunt Polly. |
| Aunt Polly | Sore toe, is it? You'll have a sore head in just one minute, if you don't get to whitewashing this fence! |
| Tom | All right, Aunt Polly! All right! Just let me get up. I'll do it! |
| Aunt Polly | You'll do it, and no more of your nonsense, Tom Sawyer! No more of your nonsense! Do you hear me? |
| Tom | Just put your shoe on, Aunt Polly. I hear you. |
| Aunt Polly | I never did see a boy like you, Tom Sawyer. I never did. Lazy! That's all! Just plain lazy! *(And she exits.)* |

| | |
|---|---|
| Announcer | Tom picked up his brush. He looked at the fence. His heart certainly wasn't in his job. His mind was on the well, where the boys and girls were having all sorts of fun. He thought of the million other things he would prefer to do. He looked into his pockets to see what he had, hoping he had put away something he could exchange for a half an hour of freedom. He didn't have a thing of any value at all. Jim had run off with his white marble. Then, all of a sudden, just as Ben Rogers came into sight, he had an inspiration. |
| Ben | (Enters, eating an apple and pretending he is a steamboat) Ding-dong-dong, ding-dong-dong. (As he reaches Tom) Stop her, sir! Ting-a-ling-ling! Set her back on the stabboard! Ting-a-ling-ling! Stop the labboard! Ting-a-ling-ling! Out with your spring-line! Lively now! Done with the engine, sir! Ting-a-ling-ling! Sh! Sh! Sh! (He looks at Tom, who has paid him no attention at all.) Hey! Are you a stump or something? |
| Tom | (Looks at Ben, doesn't say a word, goes back to his whitewashing.) |
| Ben | You've got work to do, hey? |
| Tom | (Turning suddenly) Oh, it's you, Ben! I didn't notice! |
| Ben | I was making enough noise. (Playing the steamboat again) Ship up to back! Ting-a-ling-ling! Right, sir! Ting-a-ling-ling! |
| Tom | I thought it was a steamboat. |

**Ben**  It was! I'm the steamboat! And you're whitewashing the fence.

**Tom**  That's what I'm doing.

**Ben**  I'm going swimming!

**Tom**  That's good.

**Ben**  Don't you wish you could go swimming?

**Tom**  No.

**Ben**  No? You'd rather be working, I suppose?

**Tom**  Working?

**Ben**  Whitewashing the fence! That's working!

**Tom**  Not for me, it isn't.

**Ben**  Come on! Don't tell me you like what you're doing!

**Tom**  Why shouldn't I? You don't get the chance to whitewash a fence every day, do you?

**Ben**  I guess not.

**Tom**  Well?

**Ben**  It sure looks nice, all that whitewash. It looks clean. Say, Tom, how about letting me whitewash a little?

**Tom**  *(After a moment of thought)* No, I couldn't, Ben.

**Ben**    Why not?

**Tom**    Well, Ben, this fence is right on the street, you see. If it was the back fence, it would be different.

**Ben**    Back fence, front fence, what difference does it make?

**Tom**    Everybody can see the front fence. And Aunt Polly is awfully particular about it. I guess there isn't one boy in a thousand — maybe two thousand — that can do it the way it's got to be done.

**Ben**    Maybe! But I can do it! Let me try it, Tom! Come on! Let me try it?

**Tom**    I'd like to, Ben. Honest Indian, I would. But Aunt Polly... Jim wanted to do it, but Aunt Polly wouldn't let him. Sid wanted to do it. She wouldn't let him do it, either. See how it is, Ben? If you did something wrong, I'd be in an awful fix.

**Ben**    Oh, shucks, Tom! I'll be careful. Let me try it! I'll give you the core of my apple.

**Tom**    Well now, Ben...

**Ben**    I'll give you the whole apple! What's left of it!

**Tom**    Well, Ben...

**Ben**    Come on, Tom! Let me have a go at it!

**Tom**    You'll be careful?

| | |
|---|---|
| *Ben* | I'll be careful! |
| *Tom* | *(Taking the apple and giving Ben the brush)* Remember! You've got to be very careful, or Aunt Polly will give it to me! |
| *Ben* | Don't you worry, Tom! I'm an expert at this! |
| *Announcer* | And Ben, who had been the steamboat, began to whitewash the fence, while Tom sat down on a box, chewed on the apple Ben had given him, and watched him work. Soon, Billy Fisher came down the street. He had been flying his kite, but he stopped. |
| *Billy* | What's Ben Rogers doing, whitewashing your fence? |
| *Tom* | What are you doing, flying a kite? |
| *Billy* | I'd rather be flying a kite than whitewashing a fence. |
| *Tom* | Then go ahead and fly your kite. It isn't everybody who can whitewash this fence. |
| *Billy* | What's so special about this fence? |
| *Ben* | *(Turning around)* You've got to be careful. You've got to know how to do it. It isn't one fellow in a thousand, maybe two thousand, can do it right. You tell him, Tom. |
| *Tom* | That's right! |

| | |
|---|---|
| Billy | Yeah? Anybody can whitewash that fence. |
| Tom | You can't. |
| Billy | I wouldn't, if I could. |
| Tom | Why don't you go fly your kite, Billy? |
| Billy | I can whitewash that fence as well as Ben Rogers. |
| Ben | Not while I've got the brush. |
| Billy | I can give it a couple of licks, can't I? |
| Tom | I don't think you're good enough, Billy. I'd let you, but I don't think you're good enough. You've got to be extra careful with this fence. |
| Billy | I'll be careful. Here! Let me try it! |
| Ben | I'm whitewashing this fence! |
| Billy | But you're going to get tired, aren't you? |
| Ben | I'm not tired now, I'm not! |
| Billy | I'll wait. You'll let me paint, won't you, Tom? After Ben gets tired? |
| Tom | Well, I don't know, Billy. You've got to be very careful. |
| Billy | There's nobody more careful than I am, Tom! Come on, now! |
| Tom | Well, Billy, if it was up to me...but you know Aunt Polly. |

| | |
|---|---|
| *Billy* | There's nothing wrong with the way I whitewash. Look, Tom! I'll give you my kite if you let me have the brush a while. It isn't a new kite, but it's a good one! What do you say, Tom? |
| *Tom* | Well, if you can wait till Ben gets tired, it's all right, I guess. |
| *Billy* | I'll wait! |
| *Announcer* | Tom collected the kite. After a while, Ben did get tired. Tom watched while Billy Fisher took his turn at whitewashing the fence. Before long Johnny Miller came by, and the other fellows in the neighborhood; it was simply amazing how every-one of them wanted to whitewash that fence. By the middle of the afternoon, Tom had collected twelve marbles, a piece of blue bottle-glass, a spool cannon, a key that wouldn't unlock anything, a piece of chalk, a glass stopper, a tin soldier, a couple of tadpoles, six firecrackers, a brass doorknob, a dog collar, and more, and more, and more. Finally, Aunt Polly was called out to inspect her fence. |
| *Aunt Polly* | I don't believe it, Tom. |
| *Tom* | Come see for yourself, Aunt Polly. |
| *Aunt Polly* | Maybe a little piece of it. |
| *Tom* | All of it, Aunt Polly. |
| *Aunt Polly* | A messy job, then, Tom Sawyer! |
| *Tom* | *(As they reach the fence)* A good job! Isn't it? |

| | |
|---|---|
| *Aunt Polly* | *(Inspecting the fence)* Well! It certainly is a good job! |
| *Tom* | I'm glad you like it, Aunt Polly. |
| *Aunt Polly* | Well, I always did say that you could do a good job — if you put your mind to it. Now you can go off and play! |
| *Announcer* | So Tom Sawyer was off to play. Come to think of it, he had played all morning, and done a good job of that, too. |

# THE OUTCASTS OF POKER FLAT

## from the story by Bret Harte

*A gambler, a drunkard and two women of questionable reputation are driven from the frontier town of Poker Flat. They are joined by an innocent boy and girl who are eloping. The whole party suddenly finds itself snowbound. What is worse, the drunkard runs off with their food. How can they survive? How much courage does a gambler really have? How will the so-called "bad women" meet the possibility of death, far from any help? What happens to the innocent young boy and girl—their love and all their hopes?*

*This is one of the first stories of the Far West. It tells of a time when men truly faced the elements of nature, with not much more than their own bare hands.*

| | |
|---|---|
| THE CAST | First Man |
| | Second Man |
| | Third Man |
| | Fourth Man |
| | John Oakhurst, the gambling man |
| | The Duchess |
| | Mother Shipton |
| | Uncle Billy, the drunkard |
| | Tom Simson (Innocent) |
| | Piney Woods |
| | Crowd |
| | Announcer |
| | |
| THE SETS | Main Street, Poker Flat |
| | A camp in the mountains |

THE OUTCASTS OF POKER FLAT is an adaptation by Henry Gilfond
of the short story of the same title by Bret Harte.
This adaptation ©1966 by Henry Gilfond

*(A crowd of men stand in the Main Street of Poker Flat. They are all armed with guns. Their talk is quick and excited. John Oakhurst enters and immediately draws the attention of the crowd.)*

| | |
|---|---|
| First Man | There he is! |
| Second Man | Let's hang him! |
| Oakhurst | *(Fixing the handkerchief in his pocket)* Good morning, gentlemen. |
| Third Man | It's no good morning for you, John Oakhurst! |
| Second Man | What are we waiting for? Let's hang him! |
| Fourth Man | We've hanged two of them! What's your hurry? |
| First Man | He's a gambling man, isn't he? He took all of your money, didn't he? No more gamblers in Poker Flat! That's what we decided. Let's hang him — and now! |
| Oakhurst | *(Very cool)* It seems to me that a few of you gentlemen won some of my money, too. |
| Fourth Man | That's right. We've hanged two of them. No need to hang Oakhurst. Let's just ride him out of town with the other riff-raff. |
| Second Man | I say let's hang him! |
| First Man | Hang him! |
| Fourth Man | Let's show a little mercy. He hasn't killed anybody. He never stole a horse. |
| Third Man | No more gamblers in Poker Flat! |

| | |
|---|---|
| Fourth Man | All right. No more gamblers in Poker Flat. We ride him out of town. If he comes back, then we'll hang him. *(To John Oakhurst)* Do you hear that, Oakhurst? |
| Oakhurst | I hear you very well, sir. *(Very cool, very calm)* You may have my word on it. I shall never return to Poker Flat. |
| Fourth Man | There we have it! |
| Second Man | I still say, hang him! |

*(Another Crowd of men bring in the Duchess, Mother Shipton and Uncle Billy.)*

| | |
|---|---|
| Duchess | Please...I've done nobody any harm. Please... |
| First Man | There are the rest of them! |
| Second Man | Hang them all! That's what I say! |
| Mother Shipton | It's you they should be hanging, you and your big loud mouth! |
| Fourth Man | We've hanged two of them! That's enough to show we mean business! |
| Uncle Billy | Give me a bottle of whiskey and you can hang me from now until the snow comes, you cheap bunch of murdering thieves! |

| | |
|---|---|
| First Man | We'll hang you without the bottle, Uncle Billy! |
| Duchess | (Weeping) Please... Please... I've been a good woman. |
| Second Man | (As the crowd laughs at the Duchess) Is that what you wrote your mother? |
| Duchess | Please... |
| First Man | Hang them all! |
| Fourth Man | We're driving them out of town. |
| Mother Shipton | You're driving nobody, you big-faced slob! We're leaving! |
| Uncle Billy | There isn't a bottle in the whole rotten crowd of you, is there? |
| Duchess | Where will we go? Where are you sending us? |
| Oakhurst | Be calm, lady. Everything will be all right. |
| Duchess | (Crying) But I never did anything wrong. |
| Mother Shipton | (As the Crowd laughs at the Duchess) You didn't laugh when you were asking her favors, you big apes! |
| Uncle Billy | Couldn't squeeze a drop of whiskey out of the whole filthy pack of you! |
| Fourth Man | Let's go, now! |

| | |
|---|---|
| *Second Man* | Hang them! |
| *Mother Shipton* | Hang yourself, you scrawny pigeon! |
| *Fourth Man* | You're not to come back to Poker Flat, or you will be hanged! |
| *John Oakhurst* | We won't be back. Come, ladies. Come on, Uncle Billy. Farewell, Poker Flat. |
| *Crowd* | Good riddance! |
| *Announcer* | That was on the twenty-third of November, 1850. Poker Flat was cleaning up. They had hanged two badmen. They had driven out the gambler, John Oakhurst; the two women of questionable reputation, Mother Shipton and the Duchess; and the town drunkard, Uncle Billy. The four headed for the camp of Sandy Bar. But Sandy Bar was on the other side of the mountain and the Duchess, who was not very strong, couldn't travel very well. The party of four stopped high in the hills and made camp for the night. |
| *Uncle Billy* | *(To Oakhurst)* You haven't got a bottle, have you? |
| *Oakhurst* | A gambler never drinks. It interferes with his game. |
| *Uncle Billy* | *(Taking a bottle out of his pocket)* Then you don't want any of this? |
| *Oakhurst* | *(As Uncle Billy drinks)* I hope it doesn't snow. |
| *Uncle Billy* | *(Alarmed)* Did you say snow? |

| | |
|---|---|
| *Oakhurst* | I'm not worried about us. It's the two ladies. |
| *Uncle Billy* | *(Looking at the two sleeping women. Mother Shipton snores)* They don't look worried. |
| *Oakhurst* | It's no place to be snowbound, here in the mountains. |
| *Uncle Billy* | *(Settling down into a drunken state)* We'll all freeze to death out here if it snows. |
| *Oakhurst* | That's what I'm afraid of. |
| *Tom Simson (Innocent)* | *(Offstage)* Mr. Oakhurst! Mr. Oakhurst! |
| *Oakhurst* | *(As Innocent enters)* What are you doing here, Innocent? They didn't drive you out of town? |
| *Innocent* | No, sir. Why should they drive me out of town? *(Suddenly realizing why Oakhurst is up in the mountains)* Why would they do that to you, Mr. Oakhurst? They had no right! |
| *Oakhurst* | I told you never to gamble, didn't I, Innocent? |
| *Innocent* | But you gave me back every cent you won from me, Mr. Oakhurst! |
| *Oakhurst* | That's because you are such an innocent, Tom. I didn't make a habit of giving people back the money I won from them. Are you here alone, Innocent? |

| | |
|---|---|
| Innocent | No, sir. Do you remember Piney Woods, sir? Her father wouldn't let us get married, so we've run away. We've eloped. We're going to get married in Poker Flat. *(As Piney Woods enters)* Isn't she pretty, Mr. Oakhurst? |
| Uncle Billy | She sure is! |
| Oakhurst | *(To Uncle Billy, sharply)* They're getting married! *(To Innocent)* You had better get moving, if you want to get to Poker Flat before dark. |
| Innocent | We'd just as soon camp here for the night, Mr. Oakhurst. *(To Piney)* Wouldn't we, Piney? |
| Piney | It's romantic. |
| Oakhurst | We may be getting some snow, Innocent. Better push along. |
| Innocent | *(Disappointed)* You don't want us here? They didn't throw you out of Poker Flat. They wouldn't! You just don't want us here. |
| Oakhurst | There isn't enough food for all of us. |
| Innocent | Oh, I've got plenty of food. I've got an extra mule out there, with all the others. *(Pointing)* And there's a little cabin Piney can stay in with *(indicating the Duchess)* Mrs. Oakhurst. |
| Uncle Billy | *(Beginning to laugh)* Mrs.... |
| Oakhurst | *(Sharply, to Uncle Billy)* Mind what you say, Uncle Billy! |

*The Outcasts of Poker Flat* **63**

| | |
|---|---|
| Uncle Billy | (*Sobering up a little*) I was just thinking about the mule with all the food it was carrying. |
| Innocent | There'll be plenty for all of us. |
| Oakhurst | Of course. I just hope we don't get any snow. |
| Announcer | John Oakhurst hoped, but hoping didn't help. Snow came in the morning when everyone but Oakhurst was asleep. |
| Oakhurst | (*Brushing the snow off his coat*) Snow! (*He looks at the sleeping figures and notices that Uncle Billy is missing.*) Uncle Billy! (*He runs to the top of a hill.*) Uncle Billy! He has taken the mules, the food — everything! |
| Innocent | (*Waking*) Mr. Oakhurst! It's snowing! It won't last long, will it? |
| Oakhurst | I hope not. |
| Innocent | Where's Uncle Billy? |
| Mother Shipton | (*Entering with the Duchess and Piney*) The mules are gone! |
| Oakhurst | I know. They must have broken away during the night. Uncle Billy is chasing after them. |
| Mother Shipton | Uncle Billy is what? More likely, the rascal has... |
| Oakhurst | (*Aside to Mother Shipton*) He has run off with them. But Innocent doesn't have to know that yet, does he? |

| | |
|---|---|
| Mother Shipton | But he has all the food with him! What are we going to do for food? |
| Oakhurst | I've hid some. Enough to last a week, maybe. |
| Mother Shipton | That no good… |
| Oakhurst | None of us, Mother Shipton, if you ask Poker Flat, is any good. The kids will get the whole story soon enough. Let them keep their innocence just a little while longer. It won't hurt you. Besides, it might frighten them to know the truth. You don't want to frighten them, do you? |
| Mother Shipton | No. They're nice kids. The two of them. |
| Oakhurst | *(To Innocent)* I'll go and help Uncle Billy find those mules, before the snow gets too deep. |
| Innocent | I wouldn't worry about those mules, Mr. Oakhurst. The snow isn't going to last. Even if it does, it's nice and comfortable here. The snow has got to melt some time. Then we can all go back to Poker Flat together. |
| Oakhurst | Sure, sure. *(He exits.)* |
| Innocent | *(To Piney)* I told you that you'd like Mr. Oakhurst. He's good and kind. And he's brave, too. |
| Piney | I can't wait to get to Poker Flat. *(To the Duchess)* I've heard such wonderful stories about Poker Flat. All the good things they have in their fine stores….But I guess you're used to all that by now. |
| Mother Shipton | You talk too much, Piney Woods. |

| | |
|---|---|
| *Piney* | I was just thinking about Poker Flat. |
| *Mother Shipton* | Then just go on thinking about it, but keep your lips to yourself. |
| *Innocent* | We can sing, can't we? |
| *Mother Shipton* | If you have to. |
| *Innocent* | I like to sing. *(He begins to sing.)* "I'm proud to live in the service of the Lord, And I'm bound to die in His army." *(As John Oakhurst enters)* Mr. Oakhurst! Did you find them? |
| *Oakhurst* | The snow is too thick. There's no trail. |
| *Mother Shipton* | That's a fine state of affairs! |
| *Duchess* | *(Beginning to weep again)* What are we going to do? |
| *Oakhurst* | We'll manage. |
| *Mother Shipton* | How? |
| *Innocent* | If Mr. Oakhurst says we'll manage, then we'll manage. Isn't that right, Piney? |
| *Piney* | If you say it's right, Tom, it must be right. |
| *Mother Shipton* | Stop all that love slobbering. I'm not used to it any more. *(To Oakhurst)* Sit down. You must be tired. |
| *Oakhurst* | No, I'm not tired. |
| *Mother Shipton* | You will be, soon enough. |

| | |
|---|---|
| *Oakhurst* | Never. A gambler, a poker player, never gets tired — not when he is running a streak of luck. |
| *Mother Shipton* | Nothing lucky about this snow and these mountains. |
| *Oakhurst* | No. The cards have been against us. Luck's been bad, Mother Shipton, but stick with your cards. Luck's bound to change. Do you know why? |
| *Mother Shipton* | No. Tell me why. |
| *Oakhurst* | "For I'm proud to live in the service of the Lord, And I'm bound to die in His army." |
| *Announcer* | John Oakhurst put up a brave front, but his courage couldn't stop the snow from falling. It fell all that day, and the next day, and the next day. Food began to run low. The rations became smaller and smaller. At midnight, on the tenth day of the storm, Mother Shipton, weak and fading, called John Oakhurst to her side. |
| *Mother Shipton* | *(On her bed)* I'm going, John. |
| *Oakhurst* | Nonsense! The snow is going to stop and we'll be moving again. |
| *Mother Shipton* | No, John. I'm not going to be moving again. I'm dying. |
| *Oakhurst* | It's a bad dream, Mother Shipton. |
| *Mother Shipton* | It's been a bad dream, but I'm not dreaming any more. Don't wake the kids. Here! Take the bundle from under my head, and open it. |

| | |
|---|---|
| Oakhurst | *(Taking the bundle and opening it)* It's all your rations! You haven't eaten for a week! |
| Mother Shipton | Hush! Give it to the kid. Give it to Piney. |
| Oakhurst | You've starved yourself! |
| Mother Shipton | That's what they call it. *(She turns around and dies.)* |
| Announcer | They were nearing the end of their strength. They buried Mother Shipton in the morning; then John Oakhurst turned to Tom Simson, (The Innocent.) |
| Oakhurst | *(Giving Innocent a pair of snowshoes)* There's one chance in a hundred you can save her. |
| Innocent | Who? Piney? |
| Oakhurst | Piney. Put on these shoes and go down to Poker Flat for help. |
| Innocent | How about you, Mr. Oakhurst? |
| Oakhurst | I'll stay here. |
| Innocent | *(To Piney)* You heard what Mr. Oakhurst said. |
| Piney | I'll wait for you, Tom. |
| Innocent | I'll be back. |
| Piney | Hurry! |
| | *(Innocent and Piney embrace. Then Innocent exits.)* |

| | |
|---|---|
| Duchess | *(As Oakhurst follows Innocent)* **Where are you going?** |
| Oakhurst | **Just as far as the canyon.** *(He turns to go, but turns again, kisses the Duchess quickly, then leaves.)* |
| Duchess | **Can you pray, Piney?** |
| Piney | **No, Duchess.** |

*(The Duchess embraces Piney, tenderly.)*

| | |
|---|---|
| Announcer | **The wind and the snow finally stopped, but it was two days before help could come from Poker Flat, and when it did come it was too late for those who had been left in the hills. The Duchess and Piney had fallen asleep in each other's arms, and slept, and slept, and they could not hear the footsteps of the men from Poker Flat. There was peace on the faces of Piney and the Duchess when the men of Poker Flat buried them.** |

•   •   •

**At the head of the canyon, there was another sight for the men of Poker Flat. On one of the larger trees, they found a playing card, the deuce of clubs, pinned to the tree with a bowie knife.**

| | |
|---|---|
| Fourth Man | **Read it.** |
| First Man | *(Reading the writing on the deuce of clubs)* **"Beneath this tree lies the body of John Oakhurst, who struck a streak of bad luck on the 23rd of November, 1850, and handed in his checks on the 7th of December, 1850."** |
| Second Man | *(Looking at the body of John Oakhurst)* **He shot a bullet through his heart.** |
| Fourth Man | **I guess he was the strongest, and yet the weakest, of the outcasts of Poker Flat.** |

# A SERVICE OF LOVE

## from the story by O. Henry

*Joe Larrabee and Delia Caruthers had both come to New York to make their fortunes. Joe was an artist. Delia was a singer. They met, fell in love, got married, and for a while were very happy. Their only trouble was their lack of money. It takes money to study art and study singing, and very soon they had no money at all. What were they to do? Each was an ambitious artist, and each was ambitious for the other.*

*But ambition won't pay for art or singing lessons; it won't pay the rent or buy groceries, either. Delia had an idea. So did Joe. They kept these ideas secret from each other. But a little trick of fate (the usual O. Henry surprise ending) showed them how close their ideas were to each other. Really close! And isn't that the way it ought to be, with two people who are so much in love with each other?*

THE CAST     *Announcer*
                      *Joe Larrabee*
                      *Delia*

THE SET     The Larrabee apartment in a tenement house.

A SERVICE OF LOVE is an adaptation by Henry Gilfond
of the short story of the same title by O. Henry (William Sydney Porter).
This adaptation ©1966 by Henry Gilfond

| Announcer | Joe Larrabee, a very serious young man, is busy painting a beautiful picture of the Brooklyn Bridge. Delia, his wife, is at the window practicing her singing lesson. They look like a very happy young husband and wife, and they should be, because they are very much in love with each other. But soon we'll hear about a little trouble in the household. |
|---|---|
| Delia | (Singing) La, la, la la la. (She looks at Joe.) La, la, la la la. (She walks to the canvas Joe is painting.) It's pretty. |
| Joe | Do you think so? |
| Delia | No! It's beautiful! Beautiful, Joe! If I could only sing the way you paint. |
| Joe | If I could only paint the way you sing! You're the artist in this family, Delia. |
| Delia | You're the artist, Joe. |
| Joe | I wish somebody else would think so. |
| Delia | It isn't enough that I say it, is it Joe? |
| Joe | Oh, you know what I mean, Delia. I've got fifty canvases you called great. I haven't been able to sell one of them. |
| Delia | You've got to be patient. You're learning, aren't you? You're studying. |
| Joe | No more. |
| Delia | What do you mean? |
| Joe | I told the art teacher I can't go to any more of his classes. |

| | |
|---|---|
| *Delia* | Why did you do that? |
| *Joe* | It costs money to take art lessons, Delia. |
| *Delia* | So what? |
| *Joe* | So what's for dinner, Delia? |
| *Delia* | We've got some bread and some cheese. |
| *Joe* | You know what I mean. And you've given up your singing lessons. |
| *Delia* | I can pick them up again. |
| *Joe* | Sure! |
| *Delia* | Oh, let's not quarrel, Joe. |
| *Joe* | I won't quarrel. I'll just go out and get a job. |
| *Delia* | No you won't! You're an artist, and you're going to stay an artist! I'm going to give singing lessons. |
| *Joe* | Singing lessons? To whom? |
| *Delia* | You don't think I'm good enough to give singing lessons? |
| *Joe* | Sure, but... |
| *Delia* | ...where am I going to find people who want to take lessons from me? |
| *Joe* | That's it, I guess. |
| *Delia* | Well let me tell you, Joe Larrabee, all I need to do is to say the word and I'll have more students than you can count. |
| *Joe* | When did this happen, Delia? |
| *Delia* | It's been happening. It's been happening all along. So you just stick to your painting. That's where you belong. |

*A Service of Love* **73**

**Joe** And how about your singing lessons?

**Delia** I'll take them, too. Now don't you worry another minute about anything. Just finish that beautiful bridge you're painting.

**Announcer** And Delia went out to look for somebody — anybody — who wanted to learn how to sing and would pay her to teach them. For the first few days she couldn't find a soul who was interested in music, never mind learning how to sing. But on the fourth day, she came home with spirits high, and with money in her purse.

**Delia** (Happily) I've got a pupil, Joe! She is beautiful! And the loveliest people!

**Joe** (He is at the easel and about to put down his brush) Tell me all about it, Delia!

**Delia** You keep painting! I'll tell you all about it, but you keep painting.

**Joe** Now, Delia. This isn't quite fair.

**Delia** Keep painting, Joe Larrabee, or I won't say another word.

**Joe** All right. I'll keep painting. Go ahead. Tell me.

**Delia** Well, you'll never guess. It's Clementina Pinkney!

**Joe** Who is she?

**Delia** You don't know? Oh, Joe! She's General Pinkney's daughter. General A. B. Pinkney!

**Joe** I've never heard of him, either.

| | |
|---|---|
| *Delia* | Well, you should have heard about him. You'll hear all about him now, at any rate. They live in the most beautiful house on Seventy-first Street. And you should see what it looks like inside! |
| *Joe* | I can guess. |
| *Delia* | Oh no, you can't. It's so rich! And Clementina is so beautiful. She's a delicate thing. She always dresses in white and has the most delicate manners. |
| *Joe* | Can she sing? |
| *Delia* | Like a bird. I'm giving her three lessons a week, and they're paying me five dollars a lesson. Think of it, Joe! Five dollars a lesson! |
| *Joe* | That's not so bad, I suppose. |
| *Delia* | Bad? Joe! Two or three more pupils like Clementina and I'll be able to go back to my own singing lessons. |
| *Joe* | That's fine. That's fine. |
| *Delia* | You don't seem to be very happy about it, Joe. |
| *Joe* | I'm not. |
| *Delia* | I thought you'd be very happy. Five dollars, three times a week; that's fifteen dollars. |
| *Joe* | How far do you think that'll carry us? |
| *Delia* | It's fifteen dollars more than we had before. |

**Joe**  That's great! And what do you think I'm going to do, with my wife running around to make fifteen dollars a week?

**Delia**  There'll be more when I get more pupils.

**Joe**  Sure. You'll do the work, and I'll be messing around with my paints and canvas. Not on your life!

**Delia**  But we made a bargain, Joe.

**Joe**  We made no such thing. If you can work, I can work. I'll sell papers or lay bricks. I've got two strong hands, and my feet are good. I'm going to use them.

**Delia**  Please, Joe! I want you to keep going to your art class. I haven't quit music. Everybody who sings teaches at some time or other. Maybe I've started a little early, but I'm still with my music. Don't stop now, Joe. We'll get along with this money I make giving lessons. And you must go on with your painting. Please, Joe.

**Joe**  All right. If that's the way you really want it. But I don't like your giving lessons.

**Delia**  When one loves art, there isn't ever too much one can do for it.

**Joe**  No. I guess not. My teacher liked the painting of the bridge.

**Delia**  I knew he'd like it. It's good.

| Joe | And Tinkle, the art dealer, said I could hang a couple of my pictures in his gallery. |
|---|---|
| Delia | That's wonderful, Joe! Why didn't you tell me? |
| Joe | Nobody has bought anything yet. |
| Delia | No, but they will. |
| Joe | Maybe. There may be some idiot with a lot of money who likes them. |
| Delia | They'll like them, Joe. They'll buy them. And until then, we've got General Pinkney and this veal roast his five dollars bought for us! |
| Announcer | At the end of the next week, Delia came home rather tired. She had good reason to be tired. |
| Delia | I wish Clementina would practice more. I keep telling her the same things over and over again. It is tiring. And she always dresses in white. I wish she would wear pink or blue or black once in a while. |
| Joe | (Who is more cheerful than usual) You can't do anything about it, can you? |
| Delia | No. But the General is a dear. He comes into the room, plays with his little white beard, and listens. Just listens. Clementina has such a funny little cough. I hope she is stronger than she looks. I'm really getting attached to her. She is so gentle and high-strung. The General is a widower, you know. His brother was once the Ambassador to Bolivia. Why aren't you saying anything, Joe? |

| Joe | (Taking some money from his pocket and putting it down on the table) I sold a painting. |
|---|---|
| Delia | Oh, Joe! You sold a painting! |
| Joe | To a man from Peoria. |
| Delia | Oh, Joe! I'm so happy for you! |
| Joe | I wish you could have seen him, Delia. A fat man with a woollen muffler. He bought the obelisk — thought it was a windmill! I told him it was an obelisk and he bought it anyway. |
| Delia | Oh, Joe! |
| Joe | And he ordered another. He wants a painting of the railroad. Music lessons? I guess painting still brings in the money! |
| Delia | I knew it! I knew it! I knew you would sell your paintings! Aren't you glad, Joe, that you didn't quit your art lessons? Look at all the money we have! Let's have a real dinner tonight! |
| Joe | Oysters! |
| Delia | And steak! Oh, my Joe! |
| Announcer | It was a happy scene. Art, it seemed, had won out. Joe could continue with his painting lessons. Delia could continue with her singing lessons. But not everything is what it seems to be. Let's get back to Joe and Delia, one week later. Joe is already home, his money on the table. Delia enters with her right hand in bandages. |

| | |
|---|---|
| Joe | What's this? |
| Delia | *(Laughing, but not very happily)* Nothing. Nothing at all. |
| Joe | What do you mean? Your hand is all wrapped up in bandages. What did you do to it? What happened? |
| Delia | I tell you, Joe, nothing. Clementina wanted some Welsh rabbit after her lesson. I told you that she's a queer girl. |
| Joe | And the rabbit bit your hand? |
| Delia | Oh, Joe! Now you're being silly. |
| Joe | All right. I won't be silly. What happened to your hand? |
| Delia | I told you. Clementina wanted some Welsh rabbit. She's nervous and she spilled it on me, while she was serving it. It was red hot. Boiling. |
| Joe | It must hurt! |
| Delia | It hurt then. It's not too bad now. Clementina was sorry. She was very sorry. But you should have seen the General! He rushed downstairs and sent the furnace man to the drugstore for some oil and things to bind it up with. It hurt awfully, Joe. It isn't too bad right now. |
| Joe | *(Pulling something loose from Delia's bandage)* What's this? |
| Delia | Something soft that had oil on it. *(Seeing the money on the table)* Oh, Joe! Did you sell another painting? |

| | |
|---|---|
| Joe | Did I? Just ask the man from Peoria. He loved the railroad picture. He wants another one. He wants a painting of the Hudson River to take back to Peoria. What time did you burn your hand, Delia? |
| Delia | Five o'clock. Right after the lesson. The iron... I mean the rabbit came off the fire about...five o'clock. You should have seen the General... |
| Joe | Sit down, Delia. |
| Delia | *(Sitting)* I am tired, Joe. |
| Joe | I'm sure you're tired. Tell me, Delia. What have you been doing these last two weeks? |
| Delia | Why, you know! I've told you. There are the lessons for Clementina and... |
| Joe | Delia. What have you been doing these past two weeks? |
| Delia | Oh, Joe... |
| Joe | Now tell me. |
| Delia | I haven't been giving anybody any lessons. |
| Joe | I know that. |
| Delia | I just couldn't get any pupils, and I just couldn't bear to have you give up your art lessons. There's no Clementina. There's no General Pinkney. I got a job ironing shirts in that big Twenty-fourth Street Laundry. That's where I got this burn. Some girl set a hot iron on my hand. You're not angry, Joe? If I hadn't got the work, you mightn't have sold the pictures to the man from Peoria. You're not angry, Joe? |

Joe     He doesn't come from Peoria.

Delia    I don't care where he comes from. How did you know I wasn't giving music lessons to Clementina?

Joe     I didn't. Not till tonight. And I wouldn't have known, except I sent this cotton waste and oil from the engine room this afternoon for a girl upstairs who had her hand burned by an iron. You see, Delia, I've been working the engine in that laundry on Twenty-fourth Street for these last two weeks.

Delia    Then the story about the pictures you sold...

Joe     Like your story about the music lessons. My man from Peoria and your General Pinkney are made of the same stuff. Something we created with our minds, eh, Delia?

Delia    Joe! *(She begins to laugh, and Joe begins to laugh, too.)*

Joe     When one loves art...no service seems...

Delia    Stop right there. You haven't got it right.

Joe     No?

Delia    No. It's just: when one loves, there isn't too much one can do for the person one loves.

Joe     *(Laughing)* General Pinkney! Clementina!

Delia    The man from Peoria!

       *(THEY BOTH LAUGH.)*

# EFFIE WHITTLESY

## from the story
## by George Ade

*Ed Wallace comes home to find that his wife has hired a new servant. This isn't strange, because servants come and go. But the new servant is an old friend of Ed's, a girl he used to take to parties when he was a boy in a small town. This makes quite a difference, especially when Effie Whittlesy, the new servant, insists on calling Ed Wallace by his first name. This is natural enough for Ed and for Effie, but Mrs. Wallace comes from high society and she is shocked, not only by the familiar manner in which her servant addresses her husband, but also by their small talk about the people "back home."*

*A family crisis develops. Ed doesn't mind being called Ed, and Effie can't call him anything else, but Mrs. Wallace won't have it, no matter how good a servant Effie is. What is to be done? Will Effie be forced to call Ed, Mr. Wallace? Will Mrs. Wallace fire Effie? Will Mr. Wallace allow his wife to fire his old, home-town friend?*

THE CAST    Mrs. Wallace
                  Mr. Wallace
                  Effie Whittlesy

THE SET    The Wallace dining room

EFFIE WHITTLESY is an adaptation by Henry Gilfond
of the short story of the same title by George Ade.
This adaptation ©1966 by Henry Gilfond

| | |
|---|---|
| *Mrs. Wallace* | *(As Mr. and Mrs. Wallace enter the dining room)* Look how nicely she has set the table! |
| *Mr. Wallace* | Where did she come from? |
| *Mrs. Wallace* | The agency sent her. She is from the country somewhere. and she is a jewel. She went to work the minute she took her coat off. You should see the kitchen. It sparkles. |
| *Mr. Wallace* | That's the way they always begin. |
| *Mrs. Wallace* | This one is different, I'm sure. She doesn't want any nights off. She won't go out after dark. What do you think of that? |
| *Mr. Wallace* | It sounds too good to be true. You had better pay her anything she asks for. Put lace curtains in her room. Buy her all the papers and magazines she wants to read. |
| *Mrs. Wallace* | I would, if she would read them. I don't think she would. |
| *Mr. Wallace* | Can't read, eh? |
| *Mrs. Wallace* | I didn't ask her, but I don't think she'd have the time. Every time I looked into the kitchen, she was working away, singing some country song. |
| *Mr. Wallace* | Ho! Ho! I knew there was some hitch to it. She sings, does she? |
| *Mrs. Wallace* | We can always shut the doors. Besides, her voice isn't that bad, and she sings quietly. |
| *Mr. Wallace* | We'll see. How does she cook? |

**84**  *Effie Whittlesy*

| | |
|---|---|
| Mrs. Wallace | *(As they sit down to the table)* It smelled good in the kitchen. *(Ringing the table bell)* We'll find out soon enough. |
| Mr. Wallace | *(Picking up a glass of water)* Well, here's hoping. *(He is about to drink his water, but he stops short as Effie enters. He looks at Effie and he can't quite believe what he sees.)* Well, By George! |
| | *(Effie comes in with a plate in her hand, looks at Mr. Wallace, gives him a little frightened smile, and quickly puts the plate on the table.)* |
| Mr. Wallace | You aren't Effie Whittlesy, are you? |
| Effie | *(Really surprised)* For heaven's sake! |
| Mr. Wallace | You don't know me, do you? |
| Effie | Ed! Ed Wallace! That's who you are! Ed Wallace! |
| Mr. Wallace | *(As Mrs. Wallace looks on with amazement, he reaches out his hand to Effie.)* Effie Whittlesy! |
| Effie | *(Shaking hands with Mr. Wallace)* Of all things! |
| Mr. Wallace | *(To Mrs. Wallace)* This is Effie Whittlesy. She's from my home town. We used to go to school together. She used to work for my mother every once in a while, help with the housework and cooking. I haven't seen her since...*(To Effie)* I didn't know you were in the city. When did you get here? |
| Effie | Oh, I came here about a year ago. Well! Ed Wallace! There are so many Wallaces. But I knew it was you the minute I looked at you! Who would believe it? *(To Mrs. Wallace)* We saw a lot of each other, back home. |

| | |
|---|---|
| Mr. Wallace | It's good to see you again, Effie. |
| Effie | I came here to visit Mort's people. I suppose you know he's driving a bus. He's doing real well. I didn't want to be a burden to him, so I got myself a job working for Mr. Sanders. He's a railroad man, lives on the North Side. It was all right, but he wanted me to serve liquor. I'd just as soon handle a toad as handle a bottle of beer. I left. Liquor just ruined Jesse. You remember Jesse. He's gone to the dogs. He's been with a circus somewhere these last two years. |
| Mr. Wallace | The family is all broken up, eh? |
| Effie | Gone to the four winds since Mother died. Of course you know that Laurie married Huntford Thomas. They're doing as well as you can expect, with Huntford as lazy as he is. |
| Mr. Wallace | So that's what's happened to the family? |
| Effie | Yes, that's what's happened. Life just keeps changing. |
| Mrs. Wallace | That will be all for now, Effie. |
| Effie | (Startled) Oh! (She exits quickly.) |
| Mrs. Wallace | Well! |
| Mr. Wallace | We were kids together. We made mud pies together and sat next to each other in the old schoolhouse. Everybody knew the Whittlesys. They were a big family—poor as church mice, but good. Effie is a good girl. |
| Mrs. Wallace | Effie! Effie! And she calls you Ed! |

| | |
|---|---|
| *Mr. Wallace* | Why shouldn't she? She always called me Ed. Everybody called me Ed. She never heard me called anything else. |
| *Mrs. Wallace* | She'll have to call you something else here! You had better tell her that, too! |
| *Mr. Wallace* | Oh, no! Don't ask me to do that. I can't put on any airs with Effie Whittlesy. She's seen me licked at school. She's been at our house every time Mother was sick and needed some help. She's almost like a member of my own family. |
| *Mrs. Wallace* | Well, she's not a member of this family! |
| *Mr. Wallace* | Come on, now. I used to take her to parties and singing lessons. I'd hate to have her go back to the old town and tell them that I was too stuckup to remember old times and made her call me "Mr. Wallace." You never lived in a small town, did you? |
| *Mrs. Wallace* | No. I never enjoyed that privilege. |
| *Mr. Wallace* | Well, it may be a privilege to live in a small town, but it certainly doesn't help a man become a snob. |
| *Mrs. Wallace* | You're not a snob when you correct a servant! And a servant doesn't call you by your first name! "Ed!" Well, I never! And you used to take her to parties and singing school! |
| *Mr. Wallace* | Twenty years ago! You're not surprised, are you? You knew when you married me that I was brought up on a farm, that I worked my way through college. I'll admit that my past doesn't exactly make me right for high society, but it will be great if I ever go into politics. |

| | |
|---|---|
| *Mrs. Wallace* | I know all about your past history. It doesn't bother me. But I was just thinking of how pleasant it will be when we have a dinner party, and *she* comes in and calls you Ed! |
| *Mr. Wallace* | *(Laughing)* That would shock the neighbors, wouldn't it? |
| *Mrs. Wallace* | I really don't think you'd care. *(She rings the bell for Effie.)* |
| *Mr. Wallace* | She won't hurt us any. If she's a little behind in her manners, she'll learn. |
| | *(Effie enters, with the second course of the dinner, and there is a moment of silence, as she sets it on the table.)* |
| *Mr. Wallace* | *(To Effie)* Do you get the home-town papers? |
| *Effie* | Every week. |
| *Mr. Wallace* | I hear there's been a lot of sickness this winter. Lora wrote me that your Uncle Joe hasn't been well. |
| *Effie* | He's better now. |
| *Mr. Wallace* | That's good. |
| *Effie* | Mort was wondering about you the other day. He said he hadn't seen you for a long time. You certainly have a nice house here. *(She exits quickly.)* |
| *Mrs. Wallace* | "You certainly have a nice house here!" |
| *Mr. Wallace* | It is a nice house, isn't it? |
| *Mrs. Wallace* | She can't stay here. She'll have to go. |

| | |
|---|---|
| Mr. Wallace | Why? She cooks well. She cleans well, you said. |
| Mrs. Wallace | I'll not have any servant call you Ed! I suppose you'll be inviting that bus driver, whatever his name is, and that beerdrinking railroad man from the North Side? I suppose you'll be in the kitchen, next, helping wash the dishes? |
| Mr. Wallace | Why not? |
| Mrs. Wallace | Because you're Mr. Edward Wallace! That's why not! And no servant in my house will call you anything but Mr. Wallace. I'll give her a good talking to. That's what I'll do. I'll tell her it's Mr. Wallace, or else she can go! |
| Mr. Wallace | Don't do that. I'll talk to her. |
| Mrs. Wallace | And what will you say? |
| Mr. Wallace | I'll find something to say. Don't you worry. |
| Mrs. Wallace | She is not to call you Ed. |
| Mr. Wallace | I'll take care of it. |
| Mrs. Wallace | It's most embarrassing. *(She rings the table bell.)* Tell her I'll have my coffee in the living room, if it's all right with you. |
| Mr. Wallace | *(As Mrs. Wallace prepares to leave)* It might be better. |
| Mrs. Wallace | "Ed!" *(And she exits as Effie enters.)* |
| Effie | *(After Mrs. Wallace is gone)* Is something wrong? |
| Mr. Wallace | No, no! Everything is fine, Effie. Everything is fine. Mrs. Wallace wants her coffee in the living room. |

| | |
|---|---|
| *Effie* | She isn't pleased. |
| *Mr. Wallace* | She's pleased. She's pleased, all right. *(Changing his tone)* Effie! How long is it since you've seen Lora? |
| *Effie* | Oh, not since I left home. |
| *Mr. Wallace* | That's a long time. More than a year, isn't it? |
| *Effie* | More than a year. |
| *Mr. Wallace* | Why don't you visit her for a while? She'd be glad to see you. Why don't you go down there for about a month or so? |
| *Effie* | I'd like to, Ed. I can't afford it. |
| *Mr. Wallace* | Oh, I'll buy you the railroad ticket, and it will cost you hardly anything to live back home. |
| *Effie* | That's right. A dollar goes a lot farther there than it does in this big city. But I can't. |
| *Mr. Wallace* | You can, if you want to. |
| *Effie* | How about Mrs. Wallace? |
| *Mr. Wallace* | It would be fine with her. |
| *Effie* | I mean, how is she going to get any help? She told me she had an awful time, trying to get someone right. I couldn't do it to her, Ed. |
| *Mr. Wallace* | Well, to tell you the truth, Effie, I just don't like the idea of your being in my house as a — well, as a hired girl. |
| *Effie* | I don't see that that should bother you, Ed. I used to work for your Ma. Now, I'm working for you. Nothing has really changed. The work is the same. |

| | |
|---|---|
| *Mr. Wallace* | That's not it, Effie. When you come to my house, I'd like you to come as a guest, not as a servant. |
| *Effie* | That doesn't make any sense, Ed Wallace. I'd just as soon work for you as anyone else. A lot sooner. |
| *Mr. Wallace* | I know, Effie. But I don't like to see my wife giving orders to an old friend like you. You understand, don't you, Effie? |
| *Effie* | No, Ed, I don't understand. But I'll quit, if that's what you want me to do. |
| *Mr. Wallace* | Come on now, Effie. I'll buy you that railroad ticket and you can take the train for home tomorrow. |
| *Effie* | I'll go, if that's the way you see it. I'd like to go back home for a while. |
| *Mr. Wallace* | And when you get back, if you come back, I'll get you a dozen places you can work in. |
| *Effie* | Ed Wallace. They'll never believe it, when I tell them. |
| *Mr. Wallace* | You'll tell them, though, won't you? |
| *Effie* | I certainly will. *(She exits.)* |
| *Mrs. Wallace* | *(Entering)* Aren't you going to join me in the living room? For Coffee? |
| *Mr. Wallace* | Sure. |
| *Mrs. Wallace* | You spoke to her? To Effie? |
| *Mr. Wallace* | I spoke to her. |
| *Mrs. Wallace* | Well, I hope she won't be calling you Ed any more. |
| *Mr. Wallace* | Not for long. She's leaving. |

| | |
|---|---|
| Mrs. Wallace | Oh? |
| Mr. Wallace | I'm buying her a ticket, so she can go back home for a while. |
| Mrs. Wallace | That's very nice of you. |
| Mr. Wallace | But she'll be back. |
| Mrs. Wallace | Not if she doesn't call you Mr. Wallace! |
| Mr. Wallace | I don't think she'll do that. |
| Mrs. Wallace | Then I won't have her working here! Not here! |
| Mr. Wallace | You don't understand. She won't be working here. I've asked her to call, when she comes back. |
| Mrs. Wallace | To call! Here? |
| Mr. Wallace | Here. Of course. This is where we live, isn't it? And I told her that you would be delighted to see her. |
| Mrs. Wallace | No! Did you really invite her? |
| Mr. Wallace | Of course. And I'm sure she'll be coming, too. |
| Mrs. Wallace | Oh! What will I do? What will I do? |
| Mr. Wallace | I'm sure you'll do all right. I'm sure you'll manage it, even though you don't come from a small town out in the country. |
| Mrs. Wallace | (Smiling at last) Oh, Ed! Ed! You do have faith in me, don't you? |
| Mr. Wallace | I do, Mrs. Wallace. I do. |

# THE BRIDE COMES TO YELLOW SKY

## from the story by Stephen Crane

*Jack Potter, marshall of Yellow Sky, is bringing his bride home from San Antonio. He is worried about how his friends will greet him, and how they will feel about their marshall being married. But his friends will not be at the station. Instead, he will be met by a gunshooting drunk, Scratchy Wilson, who has sworn to get the marshall. They will confront each other, Scratchy with his two guns in his hands and the marshall unarmed.*

*Here is a story of the old Wild West, where anything could happen, and generally did. This account of the meeting between two sworn enemies, when Jack Potter brings his bride to Yellow Sky, has both humor and suspense.*

| THE CAST | Announcer | Drummer |
|---|---|---|
| | Jack Potter | Bartender |
| | The Bride | Young Man |
| | The Train Porter | First Man |
| | First Passenger | Second Man |
| | Second Passenger | Third Man |
| | Third Passenger | Scratchy Wilson |
| | Fourth Passenger | |

| THE SETS | Train parlor car |
|---|---|
| | Saloon |
| | Yellow Sky Street |

THE BRIDE COMES TO YELLOW SKY is an adaptation by Henry Gilfond of the short story of the same title by Stephen Crane.
This adaptation ©1966 by Henry Gilfond

| | |
|---|---|
| Announcer | This is the first of the three scenes of our playlet. Jack Potter and his Bride, a girl he has just married this morning, have boarded the train at San Antonio and are headed for Yellow Sky. They are a bit nervous, like all newlyweds; the Porter and the other passengers find them amusing. The Porter winks at the other passengers and gets a knowing wink or two in return, but the Potters are very serious. Jack and his Bride are not very young and marriage is a completely new thing for both of them. There will be something more than this to worry about when they arrive in Yellow Sky. |
| Potter | *(Smiling)* Have you ever been in a parlor car before? |
| Bride | I haven't. It's fine, isn't it? |
| Potter | Great! After a while, we'll go into the dining car and get a great dinner, the greatest dinner in the world. They charge a dollar for it. |
| Bride | A dollar? That's too much for us. Isn't it, Jack? |
| Potter | Not for our wedding trip! |
| Porter | *(Winking to a Passenger)* Newlyweds! |
| First Passenger | You can see that easily enough. |
| Second Passenger | She isn't a beauty! |
| Third Passenger | She looks as if she's been washing dishes all her life. |

*The Bride Comes to Yellow Sky* **97**

| | |
|---|---|
| Fourth Passenger | He probably got her out of some restaurant in San Antonio. |
| First Passenger | He doesn't look like too much of a bargain either, in his new store suit. He looks like a man who's next in line in a barber shop. |
| Porter | Nervous. They don't know what to do with their hands. Or their feet, either. |
| Second Passenger | Newlyweds! |
| Potter | (To his Bride) We are due in Yellow Sky at 3:42. |
| Bride | (As if surprised) Oh, we are? (She looks at her little silver watch.) |
| Potter | I bought that watch for you from a friend of mine in San Anton'. |
| Bride | It's pretty. |
| Potter | I knew you'd like it. |
| Bride | It's seventeen minutes past twelve. |
| Potter | (Calculating rapidly) We get to Yellow Sky in about three and a half hours. (He suddenly frowns.) |
| Bride | Is something wrong, Jack? |
| Potter | (Cheerfully) Everything is just great! |
| Bride | You looked worried. |

**98** *The Bride Comes to Yellow Sky*

| | |
|---|---|
| *Potter* | Oh, it's nothing. I was just thinking of Yellow Sky and how they're going to meet us. |
| *Bride* | *(Worried)* You're not expecting a crowd at the station, are you, Jack? |
| *Potter* | I wouldn't expect it. *(Strongly)* I didn't tell anyone I was going to San Anton' to get me a wife! |
| *Bride* | You're not sorry, Jack? You haven't changed your mind? |
| *Potter* | Of course not! It's just that I didn't tell anybody. I've been marshall in Yellow Sky for a long time. I guess nobody expects that the marshall will get married, that's all! |
| *Bride* | Oh! |
| *Potter* | Well, I did get married! And I'm glad I got married! |
| *Bride* | But you can't help worrying about how they'll feel about it in Yellow Sky? |
| *Potter* | *(Trying to hide his worry)* Oh, they'll like you enough in Yellow Sky. And they'll have to get used to my being married! |
| *Announcer* | The train moved on. Time went by. It was 3:42, and the train pulled into the town of Yellow Sky. |
| *Porter* | *(To Potter)* Your station, sir! |
| *Potter* | *(Picking up his bags; to his Bride)* Come on, girl! Here we are. |
| *Bride* | *(Looking out of the window)* The station is empty. |

| | |
|---|---|
| Potter | (Relieved) That's fine! We'll just walk into town. |
| Porter | (As the Potters leave) Newlyweds! |
| Announcer | We will leave the Potters for a little while now and move to the Weary Gentleman Saloon, where six men are drinking at the bar. One of the men is a drummer (a traveling salesman) and he is telling a story. |
| Drummer | ...and at the moment that the old man fell downstairs with the bureau in his arms, the old woman was coming up the stairs with two scuttles of coal. Well, of course... |
| Young Man | (Rushing into the saloon, excited) Scratchy Wilson is drunk! He's shooting away with both his hands! |
| Drummer | (As two of the men at the bar move to the rear of the saloon) Suppose he is? Come on in and have a drink. |
| Young Man | You didn't hear me, stranger! Scratchy Wilson is drunk again! Just look out for your hide! |
| Drummer | (To the Bartender) A fellow gets drunk. That's happened before. What's all the noise? |
| Bartender | You'll hear it soon enough, mister. You had better take my word for it. For the next two hours this town won't be a health resort. |
| Drummer | (Beginning to show a little worry) There isn't going to be a gunfight, is there? |
| First Man | I don't know whether there'll be a gunfight or not, but there'll be some shooting. |
| Second Man | Some good shooting! |

| | |
|---|---|
| Young Man | There'll be a gun fight fast enough, if anyone wants it. Anybody can get a fight out there in the street now. There's a fight just waiting. |
| Drummer | What did you say his name was? |
| All | Scratchy Wilson. |
| Drummer | Will he kill anybody? What are you going to do? |
| Bartender | (Boarding up the door of the saloon) I'm boarding up the door. That's what I'm doing. |
| Drummer | How often does this happen? Can he break in that door? |
| Bartender | No, he can't. He's tried it three times. But when he comes, you'd better get down on that floor, stranger. He's dead sure to shoot at the door, and a bullet may come through. |
| Drummer | Will he kill anybody? |
| First Man | He's out for trouble. I don't see any good in experimenting with him. |
| Drummer | (Completely scared) What do we do? |
| Second Man | Well, he and Jack Potter... |
| Third Man | Jack Potter is in San Anton'! |
| Drummer | Jack Potter? Who's he? |
| First Man | He's the town marshall. |
| Third Man | He goes out and fights Scratchy every time Scratchy gets himself a little too much to drink. |

| | |
|---|---|
| *Drummer* | Nice job your marshall has got! |
| *Bartender* | *(To the Drummer)* You had better get behind this bar with me. |
| *Drummer* | Thanks. I'd rather be here, where I can make a break for the back door. |
| *Bartender* | As you like. You see, this Scratchy Wilson is a perfect wonder with his gun. |
| *Second Man* | He's about the last of the old gang that used to hang around along the river here. |
| *First Man* | He's a terror when he's drunk. |
| *Bartender* | He's a different man when he's sober. Kind of simple, wouldn't hurt a fly, the nicest fellow in town. |
| *Third Man* | But when he's drunk, look out! |
| *Bartender* | I wish Jack Potter were back from San Anton'. He shot up Scratchy once. In the leg. He'd be out there now, pulling the wind out of Scratchy's sails. |
| | *(THE SOUND OF GUNSHOT)* |
| *First Man* | Here he is now! |
| *Scratchy* | *(Outside the saloon door)* Come out and fight like a man! *(He fires his gun.)* I know you're in there, Jack Potter! Come on out, you yellow-livered marshall! Come out and fight! |
| *Bartender* | *(To the Drummer)* Just be quiet. He'll go away after a while. |

| | |
|---|---|
| Scratchy | *(Firing at the door of the saloon)* Yellow! That's what you are, Jack Potter! Come out here into the open! Come on out here and fight, Jack Potter! You've got it coming to you, and you're going to get it! Come on out! *(He fires at the door again.)* |
| Bartender | He'll go away now. He knows Jack Potter isn't here. He'll go looking for him. |
| Scratchy | Jack Potter! *(Beginning to move away)* I'll find you, Jack Potter! |
| Announcer | And as Jack Potter and his Bride walked from the railroad station, into town, Scratchy Wilson prowled the streets of Yellow Sky, looking for the marshall of the town. |
| Potter | *(To his Bride)* You'll like Yellow Sky. The people are all real friendly. |
| Bride | I'm sure I'll like it. You're not worried any more? About how the town will feel, with its marshall married? |
| Potter | *(Putting up a brave front)* No! Why should I be worried? Just around the corner now, and we'll be home! |
| Announcer | But just around the corner was Scratchy Wilson, and the two men stopped short, just three paces from each other, the two guns loose in Scratchy Wilson's hands. |
| Scratchy | Tried to sneak up on me, did you? Keep your hands where they are, Jack Potter! Don't you move! Don't you move a finger to your gun! Not an eyelash! |

| | |
|---|---|
| *Potter* | Scratchy— |
| *Scratchy* | No you don't! The time has come for me to settle with you. And I'm going to do it my own way. |
| *Potter* | Scratchy Wilson! |
| *Scratchy* | Don't you move! You do what I tell you, if you don't want a gun bent on you! |
| *Potter* | I haven't got a gun, Scratchy. |
| *Scratchy* | You can't trick me, marshall! Keep your hands where they are! Don't you move! |
| *Potter* | But I haven't got a gun on me, Scratchy. |
| *Scratchy* | Don't tell me you haven't got a gun, you dog! Don't tell me any of your lies! There isn't a man in Texas ever saw you without a gun! |
| *Potter* | You'll have to do all the shooting yourself, Scratchy. I haven't got a gun. |
| *Scratchy* | *(Puzzled)* You haven't? |
| *Potter* | No. And if you're going to shoot, you'd better begin now. You'll never get a chance like this again. |
| *Scratchy* | *(Becoming sober)* If you haven't got a gun, why haven't you got a gun? Have you been to Sunday school? |
| *Potter* | I've been to San Anton'. I've just come back with my wife. I'm married. That's why I haven't got a gun. |

*The Bride Comes to Yellow Sky* **105**

| | |
|---|---|
| Scratchy | Married? |
| Potter | Married! And if I thought there were going to be any galoots like you prowling around when I brought my wife home, I'd have brought a gun! And don't you forget it! |
| Scratchy | *(Sobering fast)* You! Married! |
| Potter | Yes, married. I'm married. |
| Scratchy | *(Unable to believe what he has heard)* Not you, marshall! |
| Potter | Yes, me. And this is my wife. |
| Scratchy | This lady? |
| Potter | This lady. |
| Scratchy | *(Completely defeated, and completely sober)* Well, I suppose it's all off now. |
| Potter | It's all off if you say so, Scratchy. You know that I didn't make the trouble. |
| Scratchy | It's all off, Jack. It's all off. Married! *(And Scratchy, his guns lowered, begins to move off.)* |
| Announcer | And this is the way the Bride came to Yellow Sky. |

# A DANGEROUS GUY INDEED

## from the story by Damon Runyon

*Morgan Johnson was a dangerous man. That's what they said around town. People said he had killed ten men in New York in a gun battle—some said he killed more. People walked the other way when they saw him coming; no one would dare get into an argument with him—that is, no one but Wheezer Gambler. It wasn't that Wheezer Gambler didn't believe Morgan Johnson was a dangerous man; he just wanted to know what made him so dangerous. They say that curiosity killed the cat.*

*Now, how dangerous was Morgan Johnson, really? And was it more than curiosity that moved Wheezer Gambler to challenge the dangerous man?*

| THE CAST | Announcer | Bender |
|---|---|---|
| | Wheezer | Chandler |
| | Fowler | Bartender |
| | Shawny | Morgan Johnson |

| THE SETS | The bar |
|---|---|
| | A street in the town |

A DANGEROUS GUY INDEED is an adaptation by Henry Gilfond of the short story of the same title by Damon Runyon. This adaptation by permission of J.B. Lippincott Co., publishers of *Runyon First and Last*, from which the story is taken.
This adaptation © 1966 by Henry Gilfond

**Announcer**   Everyone in town knew that Morgan Johnson was a dangerous man, everyone except Wheezer Gambler. Wheezer took one of his handkerchiefs out of his pocket and asked questions. Wheezer always carried a couple of handkerchiefs in his pockets because he was always wheezing and sneezing. That's how he got the name Wheezer.

**Wheezer**   How do you know? Tell me. What makes this Morgan Johnson so dangerous?

**Fowler**   You just need to look at the man to know he's dangerous.

**Wheezer**   Yeah? What has he ever done in this town that makes him dangerous?

**Shawny**   It isn't what he's done, Wheezer. It's what he can do. He didn't get that scar across his nose from picking dandelions.

**Bender**   He killed ten men in New York. That's what he did. That's how he got that scar across his nose. Ten men went after him. Bad men. One zipped a bullet across his nose. That's how he got the scar. But he killed every one of them. All ten! That's a dangerous man, Wheezer.

**Chandler**   (Entering the Bar) Getting hot out there. (To the Bartender) Set them up! (To the others) Kind of quiet in here. I don't see Morgan Johnson around. Aren't you fellows drinking?

**Wheezer**   We're drinking.

**Chandler**   Oh, I know *you're* drinking, Wheezer. How come you're sober?

| | |
|---|---|
| *Fowler* | He won't be sober too long. He's fixing to ask Morgan Johnson how come he's so dangerous. |
| *Chandler* | Tired of living, eh, Wheezer? |
| *Wheezer* | Tired of the whole town shivering in its boots every time this Morgan Johnson walks the streets. |
| *Chandler* | They've got something to shiver about, Wheezer. He's a dangerous man. Killed fifteen men in New York. And he didn't need any help. |
| *Wheezer* | It was ten men, the last time I heard it. |
| *Chandler* | Fifteen, and all coming at him at once. They were shooting point blank, too. How do you think he got that scar? |
| *Shawny* | Keep away from him, Wheezer! |
| *Bender* | You never can tell when he'll let go again, Wheezer. A man like Morgan Johnson had just as soon kill a man as kill a fly. |
| *Chandler* | He's one of those quiet ones. They don't do anything, if you let them alone. Step on their toes, and you're another customer for the undertaker. |
| *Wheezer* | *(To the Bartender)* Let me have another drink. |
| *Shawny* | Haven't you had enough, Wheezer? |
| *Wheezer* | Are you going to tell me when I can drink and when I can't? |
| *Shawny* | I'm just telling you, I think you've had enough. |

| | |
|---|---|
| *Wheezer* | I know when I've had enough, and I don't need anyone telling me. Maybe I'm not your dangerous Morgan Johnson, but I don't like anyone stepping on my corns, either. |
| *Bartender* | This is the last one, Wheezer. |
| *Wheezer* | What's the matter? Don't you like my money? |
| *Bartender* | I don't like your tangling with Morgan Johnson. Some more of this whiskey, and you'll be out on the streets, looking for him. |
| *Wheezer* | You're not afraid I'm going to hurt him, are you? |
| *Bartender* | I like you, Wheezer. I'd like to see you around. |
| *Chandler* | You've had enough, Wheezer. |
| *Wheezer* | (*Drinks his whiskey*) (*To the Bartender*) Let me have another! |
| *Bartender* | No more, Wheezer. Not today. |
| *Shawny* | That's enough, Wheezer. |
| *Wheezer* | Shut up! Don't you tell me when I've had enough! |
| *Fowler* | Take it easy, Wheezer. |
| *Wheezer* | You, too! I'll show you who is dangerous! Just put up your fists! Any one of you! All of you! I'll show you who is dangerous! |
| *Bartender* | (*As Morgan Johnson enters*) All right! Break it up now! Here he comes! |
| *Wheezer* | Who comes? |

| | |
|---|---|
| *Bartender* | Morgan Johnson! |
| *Announcer* | And suddenly everyone in the bar was still, as Morgan Johnson ordered his drink. |
| *Morgan Johnson* | Make it a beer. |
| *Bartender* | It's a hot day, isn't it, Mr. Johnson? |
| *Fowler* | The sun is pretty strong for this time of the year, isn't it, Mr. Johnson? |
| *Shawny* | Works up a thirst, doesn't it, Mr. Johnson? |
| *Morgan Johnson* | I don't need the sun to work up a thirst. The sun is not that hot. It's been a whole lot hotter, I'm thinking. |
| *Fowler* | Come to think of it, it has been hotter this time of the year. I guess you're right, Mr. Johnson. |
| *Shawny* | Don't need anything to work up a sweat for a beer, does it? You can drink beer any time of the day, any time of the year. Excuse me, Mr. Johnson. *(He begins to move away.)* |
| *Morgan Johnson* | No need to apologize to me for where you're going. |
| *Shawny* | That's right, Mr. Johnson. As a matter of fact, I'm not going anywhere. Not just now, anyway. |
| *Wheezer* | Where did you get that scar, Mr. Johnson? I mean, where did you get that scar across your nose? |

| | |
|---|---|
| *Chandler* | Why don't you shut up, Wheezer? You know where Mr. Johnson got that scar, all right. We just got through telling you. *(To Morgan Johnson)* We told him, Mr. Johnson. |
| *Bartender* | Don't mind him, Mr. Johnson. He's just had a little too much to drink. |
| *Wheezer* | You're not talking, eh, Mr. Johnson? They tell me you don't talk much. |
| *Bender* | *(Trying to pull Wheezer away)* Come on, Wheezer. Let's get a little air. |
| *Wheezer* | *(Resisting)* I want to get a little information. |
| *Shawny* | Come on, Wheezer! *(Helping Bender get Wheezer out of the bar)* You're drunk! |
| *Chandler* | *(As all the men except the Bartender get Wheezer out of the bar)* Don't mind him, Mr. Johnson. He'll sober up. We'll take care of him. |
| *Bartender* | He doesn't mean any harm, Mr. Johnson. He just doesn't know how to hold his liquor. |
| *Morgan Johnson* | I guess he doesn't. He had better lay off the stuff. Might get him into a lot of trouble some day. |
| *Bartender* | He didn't mean to step on your toes, Mr. Johnson. |
| *Morgan Johnson* | No? |
| *Bartender* | You're not going to hurt him, are you, Mr. Johnson? He won't trouble you again. I'll see to it that he doesn't trouble you again. He just talks too much, Mr. Johnson. |

| | |
|---|---|
| Morgan Johnson | Too bad. Too bad. *(He finishes his drink, turns, and begins to leave the bar.)* |
| Bartender | Mr. Johnson! |
| Morgan Johnson | Yes? |
| Bartender | The Wheezer is a sick man. He's got asthma or something. He can hardly breathe, some times. |
| Morgan Johnson | Maybe the climate around here isn't too good for him. Maybe he ought to move. |
| Bartender | Yeah. I'll tell him that. I'll tell him you said it might be healthy for him to move out of here. |
| Morgan Johnson | You tell him. *(He leaves.)* |
| Bartender | *(As Shawny and Bender return)* I will, Mr. Johnson. |
| Bender | What did he say? |
| Bartender | Wheezer had better get out of town. |
| Shawny | Is that what he said? |
| Bartender | You know Morgan Johnson doesn't talk much. |
| Bender | He doesn't talk at all. |
| Bartender | Where's Wheezer now? Did you get him up to his room? |
| Shawny | No. He's out there somewhere, with Chandler. |
| Bartender | You'd better get him off the street. If he gets in Morgan Johnson's way, that'll be the end of him. |

**114** *A Dangerous Guy Indeed*

| | |
|---|---|
| *Bender* | *(Thinking aloud)* A man kills twenty people single-handed. He's dangerous! |
| *Shawny* | It was fifteen the last time I heard it. |
| *Bender* | What difference if it's fifteen or twenty! He's a dangerous man, isn't he? |
| *Shawny* | He's dangerous, all right, and poor Wheezer is going to get it. He'd just as soon kill poor Wheezer as kill a fly. |
| *Announcer* | That was Morgan Johnson's reputation. He was a hard-looking citizen, anyway you looked at him. He had a pair of black eyebrows that ran right together. His hair was black. His eyes were black. He had that scar across his nose. He never spoke about the scar, but anybody in town would tell you how Morgan Johnson was attacked by ten, fifteen, twenty badmen, all shooting away at him, and how he killed them all. When Morgan Johnson walked down the street, people always moved to the other side. If it was midnight and Morgan Johnson said it was noon, no one would disagree with him. If it was a horse and he said it was a cow, the people of the town just nodded their heads and said it was a cow. To each other they said, "Morgan Johnson is a dangerous man." |
| *Bartender* | And you're just going to stand here and have another drink, while he's out there killing poor Wheezer. |
| *Bender* | What do you want me to do? Get killed along with him? We tried, didn't we? |
| *Shawny* | Poor Wheezer. |
| *Bartender* | Yeah. Poor Wheezer. |

| | |
|---|---|
| Announcer | Suddenly there was a lot of shouting out in the street. |
| Bender | He's got him! |
| Shawny | God help Wheezer! |
| Bartender | God may help him, but I'm going out there and see what I can do about it. *(He begins to leave.)* |
| Bender | You can't help him now! |
| Bartender | I can try! *(He leaves.)* |
| Shawny | *(After a moment)* Do you want a drink, Bender? |
| Bender | No! *(He begins to leave.)* Maybe I can help, too. |
| Announcer | And Shawny and Bender joined the Bartender. There was a mob of people out on the street, but they were all sticking close to their houses. They didn't want to get in the way of any shooting, and everybody knew there was going to be shooting, with Morgan Johnson standing in the middle of the road, and Wheezer looking right up at him. Everybody was sorry for Wheezer. Everybody was sure that Wheezer was just about ready to wheeze his last, but no one was brave enough, or fool enough, to risk his neck to save the Wheezer. |
| Shawny | Look at the Wheezer. He can hardly stand on his feet. |
| Bender | He's drunk. |
| Shawny | That won't matter to Morgan Johnson. |
| Bartender | Wheezer! |
| Wheezer | *(Waving everybody away)* Shut up! Shut up! *(To Morgan Johnson)* I don't mean you! No! You keep talking! Just keep right on talking. |

| | |
|---|---|
| Morgan Johnson | You're drunk. |
| Wheezer | Sure, I'm drunk. And you're dangerous! That's what they tell me. You're a dangerous man. Well, are you a dangerous man or aren't you? |
| Morgan Johnson | Why don't you go home? You're drunk. Why don't you get off the street? |
| Wheezer | I'm drunk! Are you the dangerous man they've all been talking about? Well, what makes you so dangerous? |
| Morgan Johnson | Go home, old man. Go home. |
| Wheezer | So you're not talking. All right, you're dangerous. I'll believe them. But I want to see what makes you so dangerous. *(He pulls out a huge knife.)* |
| Morgan Johnson | What are you doing with that knife? |
| Wheezer | Why, I'm just going to cut you open and see what makes you so terribly dangerous around these parts. |
| Morgan Johnson | Oh, no you won't! |
| Wheezer | Oh, yes I will. |
| Morgan Johnson | Not with that knife, you won't! *(He turns and runs off as fast as he can, Wheezer running right after him.)* |

*A Dangerous Guy Indeed*   **117**

| | |
|---|---|
| Announcer | Wheezer never caught up with Morgan Johnson. Wheezer was drunk and besides, no man ever ran as fast as Morgan Johnson did that afternoon. As a matter of fact, he ran so fast and so far that no one in this town ever saw Morgan Johnson again. Of course, the stories about this dangerous man began to change pretty quickly, as we hear now, back in the bar. |
| Shawny | You know, I always did have my suspicions about that Morgan Johnson. |
| Bender | He never killed anybody, if you ask me. |
| Chandler | Do you really want to know how he got that scar across his nose? |
| Bartender | How? |
| Chandler | Why, he tried to steal this woman's pocketbook, in New York, and she just turned around and hit him with it. |
| Bender | That's what they're saying now. Now there's a dangerous man for you. |
| Wheezer | (Who has been sleeping off his drinks) Yeah? Well how come none of you brave guys ever tried to prove it before. |
| Bartender | (Laughs) Want another drink, Wheezer? |
| Wheezer | Sure. Just in case another dangerous man comes to town. |

**118** *A Dangerous Guy Indeed*

# THE OLD FOLKS' CHRISTMAS

## from the story by
## Ring Lardner

*Tom and Grace Carter have prepared a wonderful Christmas for their son and daughter—a big dinner and some expensive Christmas gifts. But Ted and Caroline, the son and the daughter, have their own ideas and their own plans for their school holiday. Somebody is going to be disappointed, and somebody is going to be hurt. Do Tom and Grace expect too much from their children? Are Ted and Caroline cruel to their parents? Who is to blame for the Carter Christmas?*

THE CAST      *Tom Carter*
                      *Grace Carter,* his wife
                      *Ted Carter,* their son, who has changed his
                           name from Tom, Jr., to Ted
                      *Caroline Carter,* their daughter, who has
                           changed her name from Grace to Caroline
                      *Announcer*

THE SETS      The Carter living room
                      The Carter garage

THE OLD FOLKS' CHRISTMAS is an adaptation by Henry Gilfond of the short story of the same title by Ring Lardner. It is adapted and reprinted here with the permission of Charles Scribner's Sons, publishers of *Round Up,* from which the story is taken. "The Old Folks' Christmas," copyright 1928 by Ellis A. Lardner, renewal copyright ©1956.
This adaptation ©1966 by Henry Gilfond

| | |
|---|---|
| Announcer | It is the day before Christmas. Tom and Grace Carter are sitting in their living room, waiting for their two children to come home for the holiday. In the music room there is a big Christmas tree loaded with expensive presents, but the door to the music room will remain closed until Christmas morning. There is a special present for Junior in the locked garage. |
| Tom | *(Looking at his watch)* They're a little late, aren't they? |
| Grace | They'll be along soon. The roads are crowded. Christmas, remember? |
| Tom | All the other kids have been home since the twenty-first. I don't know why Junior couldn't make it. |
| Grace | He sent us a telegram, didn't he? He had that special examination. And don't call him Junior. You know he doesn't like it. |
| Tom | All right, I'll call him Ted. Tom was good enough for me, but I have to call him Ted. And Grace had to become Caroline. I like the name Grace. Some day you'll have to tell me why she changed her name to Caroline. |
| Grace | That's the way young people are today, Tom. Don't be angry with them. Ted didn't ask for that special examination, and Caroline just couldn't leave school without finding her laundry. She's going to love that fur coat I bought her. |
| Tom | A pretty expensive coat. You never had one like it when you were twenty-one. |
| Grace | We couldn't afford it then. You couldn't afford that $300 watch you've got for Ted, either. |

**120**  *The Old Folks' Christmas*

| | |
|---|---|
| *Tom* | No, I guess I couldn't. Do you think he'll like it? |
| *Grace* | He'll love it. And the car! |
| *Tom* | Hush! We'll have to keep him out of the garage until morning. |
| *Grace* | Oh, it's going to be a beautiful Christmas, Tom. Like always. The family together... Do you think Caroline will like the opal ring and the opal earrings I bought her? |
| *Tom* | Opal is your favorite stone, isn't it? Why shouldn't she like it? And pretty expensive, too. |
| *Grace* | I know. I just couldn't think of spending all that money for myself, but for Caroline... |
| *Tom* | I think I hear them now! |
| | *(The doorbell rings. Tom and Grace rush to the door, and Ted and Caroline enter.)* |
| *Grace* | Ted! Caroline! *(She embraces them.)* Oh, Ted! You look so pale! You've been working too hard. |
| *Tom* | Looks to me like you've been drinking too hard. |
| *Grace* | Tom! How can you say such a thing? |
| *Ted* | Well, I did have a drink, Dad, but... |
| *Tom* | I know, I know. I was just teasing. Welcome home, Son. |
| *Grace* | Did you find your laundry, Caroline? |
| *Caroline* | What laundry? |
| *Grace* | The laundry you said you had lost. |

| | |
|---|---|
| *Caroline* | Oh, that. |
| *Grace* | Well, it's good to have you home for Christmas. Wash up. We'll have an early dinner, and we'll all go to bed early. We don't want to frighten Santa Claus away, do we? |
| *Ted* | Mother, I'm afraid I can't. You see, I'm going out with Herb Castle and Bernard King. We're going to see the hockey game. *(To Tom)* Is it all right, if I use your car tonight, Dad? |
| *Tom* | Why...I'm afraid not. There's something wrong with the brakes. |
| *Ted* | Too bad. I guess the Murdocks will give me a ride, won't they, Caroline? |
| *Caroline* | Sure. *(To Tom and Grace)* I'm sorry. I suppose I shouldn't have done it, but Beatrice Murdock and her brother Paul asked me to dinner and the theater tonight. I just couldn't refuse. |
| *Grace* | *(Disappointed)* I suppose you couldn't. |
| *Announcer* | And so, once again, Grace and Tom Carter sat alone in their living room, waiting for their children to come home. |
| *Grace* | *(Who has been trying to read a book)* What time is it, Tom? |
| *Tom* | You asked me that just five minutes ago. |
| *Grace* | I know, but it's long after midnight. What time is it, Tom? |
| *Tom* | Half-past two. |
| *Grace* | You don't suppose anything could have happened to them? |

| | |
|---|---|
| Tom | We'd have heard, if anything had happened to them. |
| Grace | They might have had an accident, and nobody there to report it or telephone or anything. What kind of driver is this Murdock boy? |
| Tom | Like all boys. Maybe he drives a little too fast, but he drives pretty well. |
| Grace | How do you know? |
| Tom | Oh, I've watched these boys drive. |
| Grace | Yes, but not all of them. |
| Tom | I doubt that anybody in the world has seen every nineteen-year-old boy at the wheel. |
| Grace | They're so reckless, some of them! |
| Tom | Oh, don't worry! They probably met some friends and stopped somewhere to eat something after the theater. |
| Grace | What time is it? |
| Tom | Twenty-two of. |
| Grace | Of what? |
| Tom | Of three. |
| Grace | Your watch must have stopped. Nearly an hour ago you told me it was half-past two. |
| Tom | You must have dozed off. My watch is all right. |
| Grace | I haven't closed my eyes. |

| | |
|---|---|
| Tom | Well, it's time you did. Why don't you go to bed? |
| Grace | Why don't you? |
| Tom | I'm not sleepy. |
| Grace | Neither am I. Tom, it's silly for you to stay up. I'm just waiting up to fill the Christmas stockings after the children are in bed. |
| Tom | I wouldn't be able to sleep a wink until they got home. |
| Grace | That's foolish. There's nothing to worry about. They're just having a good time. You were young once yourself. |
| Tom | That's just it! When I was young, I was young. Three o'clock! |
| Grace | Maybe they're staying at the Murdock's all night. |
| Tom | They would have telephoned. |
| Grace | Maybe they were afraid to wake us. |
| | *(The sound of an automobile stopping in front of the house)* |
| Tom | *(Rushing to the window)* Here they are! |
| Grace | I told you there was nothing to worry about. |
| Tom | His lights went out. Maybe I'd better go help him fix them. |
| Grace | No! He can fix them himself. He's just saving the battery, while he stands still. |
| Tom | Why don't they come in? |

**124** *The Old Folks' Christmas*

| | |
|---|---|
| Grace | They're probably making plans. |
| Tom | They can make them in here. I'll go tell them we're still up. |
| Grace | No! |
| Announcer | It was nearly four o'clock, when the lights in the car flashed again and Caroline walked into the house. |
| Caroline | Heavens! What are you doing up? |
| Grace | We were talking about old Christmases. Is it very late? |
| Caroline | I haven't any idea. |
| Tom | Where's Ted? |
| Caroline | Isn't he home? We dropped him at that hockey place. |
| Grace | You had better go right to bed. You must be worn out. |
| Caroline | I am, kind of. We danced after the play. What time is breakfast? |
| Grace | Eight o'clock. |
| Caroline | Oh, Mother, can't you make it nine? |
| Grace | You used to want to get up early on Christmas. |
| Caroline | I know, but... |
| Tom | You look rumpled. |
| Caroline | They made me sit in the "rumple" seat. *(She laughs.)* |

*The Old Folks' Christmas* **125**

| | |
|---|---|
| Announcer | It was all funny to Caroline, but the Christmas holiday had made a poor start for Tom and Grace Carter, and it was going to get worse. Ted arrived home at six in the morning, and it wasn't until noon that the Carter children emerged from their bedrooms. |
| Ted | *(To Caroline)* You'd better hurry. We're late. |
| Grace | Dinner is at one o'clock, children. |
| Caroline | Oh, no! We've been invited by the Murdock's for breakfast at half-past twelve! |
| Grace | But you know that we always have Christmas dinner at one, Caroline. |
| Caroline | That's too bad, Mother. I thought we'd have dinner at seven. |
| Ted | I'd forgotten it was Christmas! Where's the tree? |
| Tom | In the music room. *(He opens the door to the music room.)* |
| Caroline | Oh! It's really pretty. |
| Ted | We're late, Caroline! |
| Grace | Don't you want to see your presents? |
| Caroline | I can't open them all now, Mother. Tell me which is special. |
| Grace | *(Opens a big box)* I think you might like this one. |
| Caroline | Oh, Mother! A sealskin coat! |
| Tom | Put it on. |
| Caroline | Not now, Father. We haven't the time. |

**126** *The Old Folks' Christmas*

| | |
|---|---|
| Grace | *(Opens the box of jewelry)* Then look at this! |
| Caroline | Oh, Mother! Opals! Your favorite stone! |
| Ted | If nobody minds, I'll look at my presents later. We're late. |
| Tom | You can drive to the Murdocks, if you want to. |
| Ted | You fixed the brakes? |
| Tom | Come to the garage. |
| Ted | Mother—Dad—I'm sorry I haven't any presents for you. I was so rushed at school, and everything was closed last night. |
| Grace | Don't worry. Christmas is for young people. Dad and I have everything we want. |
| Ted | Thanks, Mother. *(He kisses her and exits with Tom.)* |
| Caroline | Mother, where did this coat come from? Would you mind horribly if I changed it for another kind of fur? |
| Grace | Of course not. You pick out anything you like, and if it costs a little more, it won't make any difference. But don't you want to wear your opals to the Murdocks? |
| Caroline | I don't think so. They might get lost. And, well, I'm not so crazy about them. |
| Grace | Oh! Well, don't worry. They can be exchanged, too. |
| Announcer | Meanwhile, Tom and Ted have entered the garage. |
| Ted | You've got two cars! |
| Tom | The new one is yours. |

*The Old Folks' Christmas* **127**

| | |
|---|---|
| Ted | Dad, that's wonderful! But it looks just like the old one. |
| Tom | Well, the old one is pretty good. Yours is better. Hop in and get her started. I filled her up with gas. |
| Ted | I'd rather drive the old one. You see, Dad, I really wanted a roadster, like Paul Murdock's. If I don't drive this new one, maybe they'll take it back, or you can make some deal for a roadster. |
| Caroline | (Entering with Grace) I just gave Mother two tickets for Jolly Jane, Father. It's the play we saw last night. You'll love it! |
| Grace | (Quietly) It's for tonight, Tom. |
| Tom | We thought we'd spend the night together. |
| Caroline | Oh you must see the play, Father! We'll be home, and the Murdocks and some friends will be dropping in. We'll dance and there'll be music. Ted and I thought you'd rather be away somewhere so our noise wouldn't disturb you. |
| Grace | We don't mind the noise, so long as you're enjoying yourselves. |
| Caroline | Oh, have yourselves a treat! And don't wait for us for supper. We'll probably be late, and you'll have to see the whole show! |
| Announcer | They were late. Tom and Grace had a rather quiet and sad Christmas supper all alone. And, as Tom had suspected, the play wasn't very good, either; and the special, after-theater dinner they tried to eat didn't make them any happier. As might have been expected, no one was home when Tom and Grace returned from their night out. The Murdocks had been there, all right, and everybody else in town, too. |

*The Old Folks' Christmas*  **129**

| | |
|---|---|
| Tom | My heavens! Look at those empty glasses. They certainly do enough drinking. |
| Grace | And smoking. |
| Tom | Cigarette butts all over the place! |
| Grace | And two big holes burned through my favorite rug! Oh, Tom! |
| Tom | They never stepped into the music room. I guess they didn't do too much dancing. |
| Grace | Tom! Tom! |
| Tom | All right, Grace. No tears now! Forget it! |
| Grace | This is one Christmas I won't forget, Tom. |
| Tom | Now look here, Grace. You haven't even opened your own present. |
| | *(Opening his box)* Well, here goes. Diamond studs and cuff buttons! |
| Grace | *(Opening her box)* An opal ring! How lovely, Tom! |
| Tom | I'm glad you like it. |
| Grace | I love it. |
| Tom | Say, we'll have to go out somewhere tomorrow night. I've got to break in these studs and buttons. |
| Grace | Well, if we're going out tomorrow night, we'd better get a good night's rest. |
| Tom | Right! I'll beat you upstairs. No waiting up tonight. I'll beat you upstairs! |

**130** *The Old Folks' Christmas*

# THE NIGHT THE BED FELL

## from the story by
## James Thurber

*James Thurber is famous for the rich humor of his great cartoons and his wonderful stories. This story is very much a Thurber story.*

*Briggs is visiting his cousin James. He quickly discovers that everything is not quite normal in his cousin's house. You'll see what Briggs means. You may also wonder how "normal" Briggs himself is.*

*This story is fun. You'll enjoy it.*

| THE CAST | James | Mother |
|---|---|---|
| | Briggs | Herman |
| | Father | (Sound Effects) |

| THE SETS | Living Room |
|---|---|
| | James' Bedroom |

THE NIGHT THE BED FELL is an adaptation by Henry Gilfond
of the short story of the same title by James Thurber. This adaptation
by permission of the producers of *A Thurber Carnival.*
This adaptation ©1966 by Henry Gilfond

| | |
|---|---|
| *Father* | I'm going to sleep in the attic tonight. |
| *Mother* | The attic is Grandfather's bedroom. |
| *Father* | But Grandfather is out fighting the Battle of Bull Run. Or is it the Indians he's fighting this time? |
| *James* | But the Civil War has been over for a long time, Father. And we don't fight the Indians any more. |
| *Father* | I know. But that isn't what your Grandfather says. |
| *Briggs* | He must be touched. |
| *Mother* | We don't speak that way about Grandfather. He just has his own ideas about things, that's all. |
| *Father* | Well, he can have his own ideas about things, fight the Battle of Bull Run, or fight Indians, and I'm going to sleep in the attic. |
| *Mother* | No, you're not. That bed in the attic is about to fall apart any minute. I don't want that bed falling down on you in the middle of the night. |
| *Father* | It has held up Grandfather all these years and will hold me up for one night. I'm going to sleep in the attic. I want to do some thinking tonight. |
| *Mother* | You can do your thinking in your own bed. I don't want the bed to fall. |
| *Father* | Don't worry so much about me. Where is Aunt Melissa? |
| *Mother* | She is already in bed. You children had better get to sleep before she starts throwing her shoes down the stairs. |
| *Father* | A very good idea. Off with you now! Off to bed! And no noise! I want to do some thinking tonight. |

**132**  *The Night the Bed Fell*

| | |
|---|---|
| James | Are you sure you want to sleep in the attic, Father? |
| Father | That is where I am sleeping. *(To Mother)* And no more talk about it. *(To the Boys)* Good night, children! |
| Briggs | Good night, Uncle. |
| James and Herman | Good night, Father. |
| Mother | I wish you wouldn't sleep in the attic, Father. |
| Father | I said that there was to be no more talk about it. |
| Mother | That bed is going to fall. |
| Father | It won't fall! Good night. *(He leaves.)* |
| Briggs | Suppose Grandfather comes home in the middle of the night, with all those Indian scalps? |
| Mother | He won't be home tonight. I hope! *(She and Herman leave.)* |
| James | And there are no Indian scalps. This isn't the first time Grandfather has gone out hunting Indians, or to fight the Battle of Bull Run. |
| Briggs | It doesn't make any sense. |
| Mother | That's enough talk now. Off to bed with you! |
| James | I hope the bed doesn't fall on Father. |
| Mother | I hope not. Now, go to bed. Sleep well, and pleasant dreams. |
| Briggs | *(To James, as they walk across the stage to their bedroom)* Why can't your father do his thinking in his own bedroom? |

| James | He always does his thinking in the attic. Doesn't everybody? |
|---|---|
| Briggs | I don't. |
| James | Then maybe you don't do any thinking. |
| Briggs | I do plenty of thinking. And what's this about the bed falling? |
| James | It's an old wooden bed. It's beginning to come apart at the seams. |
| Briggs | Then why does anybody want to sleep in it? Why don't you get a new bed? |

*(THERE IS A SOUND OF SHOES BEING THROWN DOWN THE STAIRS.)*

| Briggs | What's that? |
|---|---|
| James | That's Aunt Melissa and her shoe act. |
| Briggs | What are you talking about? |
| James | She always thinks there's a thief in the house. |
| Briggs | That's crazy! |
| James | That's only half of it. She thinks the thief is trying to chloroform her. |
| Briggs | Wow! Did she ever find one? |
| James | Find one what? |
| Briggs | A thief! A burglar! |
| James | No. But she's sure that there's one around somewhere in the house.<br>*(ANOTHER BANGING OF SHOES)* |
| Briggs | What's that? |

*The Night the Bed Fell* **135**

| James | More shoes. She doesn't care what else the thief does in the rest of the house — just so long as he doesn't slip any chloroform into her bedroom. |
|---|---|
| Briggs | She sure is nuts! |
| James | She's a little different. |
| Briggs | Nuts! But there must be a lot of people like her. |
| James | Yeah. |

*(THE SOUND OF SOMEONE SINGING "ONWARD, CHRISTIAN SOLDIERS")*

| Briggs | Who's that? |
|---|---|
| James | That's Brother Herman. He always sings "Onward, Christian Soldiers," when he's asleep. |
| Briggs | In his sleep? |
| James | That's the only time he sings it. He can't sing a note when he's awake. |
| Briggs | Everybody in this house is nuts! *(BANGING OF SHOES DOWN THE STAIRS)* Boy, oh boy! Am I glad *I'm* all right! |
| James | *(Looking at the two beds in his room, one an army cot)* Do you sleep all right? |
| Briggs | Sure. Except you'll have to wake me up every half hour. |
| James | Every half hour? How come? |
| Briggs | I don't want to choke to death, that's how come. |
| James | Choke to death? |

| | |
|---|---|
| *Briggs* | *(Setting the alarm clock)* Oh, you don't have to worry. I'm setting the alarm clock. That'll wake me up every half hour. |
| *James* | Hey! Don't do that! You'll keep everybody up all night. |
| *Briggs* | You don't want me to die in my sleep, do you? |
| *James* | Of course I don't. |
| *Briggs* | Then I'll set the alarm and I'll get up every half hour. I'm not going to die in my sleep. Not if I can help it. |
| *James* | Then I'll wake you up every half hour. You don't have to set that alarm. |
| *Briggs* | How are you going to wake me? |
| *James* | Look at this old army cot I'm sleeping on. I'll hardly get any sleep. |
| *Briggs* | Aren't you afraid you'll fall over? |
| *James* | No! But it'll make it easy for me to get up every half hour and wake you. Besides, didn't I tell you? |
| *Briggs* | Tell me what? |
| *James* | If anybody sleeping near me stops breathing, I wake up right away. |
| *Briggs* | You do? You're sure? |
| *James* | Every time. |
| *Briggs* | *(Getting into bed)* All right, then. Every half hour. You'll remember? |
| *James* | I'll remember. *(Getting into bed)* Good night. |

*The Night the Bed Fell*  **137**

| | |
|---|---|
| *Briggs* | Good night. |
| | *(There is a moment of silence, as James pretends to be asleep.)* |
| *James* | *(Suddenly)* Briggs! Wake up, Briggs! |
| *Briggs* | I'm awake. I was just holding my breath. I was testing you. I just wanted to see whether it was true, that you couldn't sleep when somebody stopped breathing. |
| *James* | *(To himself)* Well, I wasn't sleeping, either. |
| *Briggs* | What did you say? |
| *James* | Nothing. |
| | *(SOUND OF SHOES BEING THROWN DOWN THE STAIRS)* |
| *Briggs* | That's Aunt Melissa. |
| | *(SINGING OF "ONWARD, CHRISTIAN SOLDIERS")* |
| *Briggs* | That's Herman. |
| *James* | Good night. |
| *Briggs* | Good night. *(He begins to snore.)* |
| | *(SUDDENLY JAMES' BED TURNS OVER WITH A LOUD BANG, AND JAMES FALLS UNDER HIS BED.)* |
| *Briggs* | What's that? I'm dying? I can't breathe! |
| *Mother* | *(With Herman, rushing in from the next room)* Father! Father! Let's go to poor Father! The bed has fallen on him! |

| | |
|---|---|
| *Herman* | (*To himself*) Mamma must be having hysterics. (*To his Mother, reassuringly*) You're all right, Mamma! |
| *Mother* | I knew it! The bed has fallen on poor Father! Let's go to poor Father. |
| *Briggs* | Help me, somebody! I can't breathe! |
| *James* | (*Trying to get out from under his bed*) Get me out of here! |
| *Mother* | (*Banging on the door*) We're coming, Father! We're coming! |
| *Herman* | You're all right, Mamma! |
| *Briggs* | I'm choking to death! |
| *James* | (*Up on his feet at last*) What is it, Mother? |
| *Mother* | (*Still banging at the door*) Poor Father! The bed has fallen in on Father! |
| *Briggs* | I'm dying! |
| *James* | The bed fell on me, Mother. |
| *Mother* | All the way from the attic? Oh, poor Father! |
| *James* | My bed, Mother. My bed! |
| *Father* | (*Entering*) What's all this noise about? How can a man think? |
| *Mother* | Oh, you're all right! Thank heavens, you're all right! |
| *Herman* | You're all right, Mamma! |
| *James* | The bed fell on me, Mother. |

| | |
|---|---|
| *Mother* | The bed fell all the way from the attic. |
| *Father* | What bed? |
| *Mother* | Grandfather's bed. |
| *Father* | Grandfather's bed didn't fall at all! |
| *James* | It was my bed, Mother. |
| *Briggs* | I can breathe again. I'm all right. |
| *Mother* | You're all right. And Father is all right. And James is all right. |
| *Father* | Everybody is all right! Now let's get back to bed! I told you that there was some thinking I want to do. |
| *Mother* | Of course. Let's all go back to bed. Oh, I'm so glad that your Grandfather wasn't home. |
| | *(Everybody leaves except Briggs and James, who get into their beds.)* |
| *Briggs* | You'll wake me up? |
| *James* | Every half hour. |
| | *(SOUND OF SHOES BEING THROWN DOWN THE STAIRS)* |
| *Briggs* | That's Aunt Melissa. |
| | *(SINGING OF "ONWARD, CHRISTIAN SOLDIERS")* |
| *Briggs* | That's Herman. What a crazy family! |

# THE DOWNFALL OF FASCISM
# IN BLACK ANKLE COUNTY

## from the story by
## Joseph Mitchell

*This is a story about a small town in North Carolina. The title of the story is serious, and so were the two men—fat Catfish Giddy and skinny Spuddy Ransom. Catfish just wanted to be the head of an organization, any organization. Spuddy wanted an organization to throw the sinners out of Black Ankle County. When they put their strength together and went about their business, they met with something they didn't quite expect. There are lots of laughs in this story, and some surprises, too. We wouldn't give any of them away.*

| THE CAST | Announcer | Joe |
|---|---|---|
| | Spuddy Ransom, the lean one | Frankie |
| | | Willie |
| | Waters | Steve |
| | Henderson | Robert |
| | Smith | Francis Kidney |
| | Brown | Pat Kidney |
| | Catfish Giddy, the fat one | Pinky Kidney |
| | | Uncle Bowleg |
| | | |
| THE SETS | The General Store | The Kidney House |
| | High grass in Stonewall | Outside the Kidney |
| | Meeting Place | House |

THE DOWNFALL OF FASCISM IN BLACK ANKLE COUNTY is an adaptation by Henry Gilfond of the short story of the same title by Joseph Mitchell. It is adapted and reprinted here by permission of Duell, Sloan & Pearce, Inc., publishers of *McSorley's Wonderful Saloon* by Joseph Mitchell. Copyright © 1938, 1939, 1940, 1941, 1942, 1943 by Joseph Mitchell. This adaptation © 1966 by Henry Gilfond

| Announcer | The Stonewall Hardware and General Merchandise Store in Stonewall, North Carolina, was always pretty crowded. It was the place where the men of Stonewall got together when they didn't have much else to do. The men in this small town in Black Ankle County generally had very little to do, and even less ambition to do it. They just naturally walked into the General Store and sat around, talking politics and religion. Mr. Spuddy Ransom, who was a church deacon, talked louder than anyone else. |
|---|---|
| Spuddy Ransom | You ought to quit planting cotton and tobacco. You can't eat cotton and tobacco. Irish potatoes! *There's* something you ought to plant. My friends, if you can't sell your crop, you can put it on the table and eat it! |
| Waters | Did you ever try living on Irish potatoes, Ransom? |
| Spuddy Ransom | Sure! I lived a whole winter, just eating Irish potatoes. |
| Henderson | You looked kind of skinny that winter, if I remember right, Ransom. Meat! That's what a man needs to eat, if he wants to have any strength in him. |
| Spuddy Ransom | Nothing stronger than your mule, is there, Henderson? I don't see your mule eating meat any time. |
| Henderson | He doesn't eat any Irish potatoes, either, as far as I know. *(There is a general laughter; the door opens, and in walks Mr. Catfish Giddy.)* |

**144**  *The Downfall of Fascism*

| | |
|---|---|
| Catfish Giddy | Here I am, gentlemen, ugly as ever! |
| Smith | You sure have the ugliest moustache in town, Catfish! |
| Catfish Giddy | (Playing with his long moustache) Treat it with beeswax. Keeps those ends sticking out. I may not be the richest man in Black Ankle County, gentlemen, but I sure am the ugliest. You can't take that away from me. |
| Brown | There's no one trying, Catfish. |
| Henderson | How did you make out this trip, Catfish? Did you sell all that plug tobacco you carry around with you? |
| Spuddy Ransom | You ought to be selling Irish potatoes! |
| Catfish Giddy | Tobacco, Spuddy Ransom! (Becoming the town orator) Gentlemen, the glorious state of North Carolina produces so much cut plug tobacco in one year, that if you laid it end to end, it would pretty soon reach out to Egypt, or Australia, or even to the moon. |
| Smith | You tell them, Catfish! |
| Catfish Giddy | Yes, sir! In the manufacture of chewing tobacco, my friends, the Tar Heel State leads the whole civilized world! |
| Brown | More, Catfish! More! |

| | |
|---|---|
| Catfish Giddy | (Pointing to some books) There's something else I've got on my mind today, gentlemen. It's all down here in these books. Gentlemen, it's time we good citizens of Stonewall organized a branch of the Knights of the Ku Klux Klan. |
| Henderson | Not another one of your organizations, Catfish! |
| Catfish Giddy | This is different. This is the Invisible Empire. Every white man in Black Ankle County belongs in this organization. |
| Waters | But we joined up with your Stonewall Boosters, and that died after just two meetings. |
| Catfish Giddy | This is different, I tell you! |
| Smith | How about the Stonewall Chamber of Commerce? You said that was different, too. And that didn't last for more than three meetings. The Knights of the Ku Klux Klan! What's that? |
| Catfish Giddy | Read these books, gentlemen, and you'll know why you belong in the Invisible Empire. |
| Spuddy Ransom | (Who has been reading the books) It seems to make sense. |
| Catfish Giddy | Good sense! Remember, gentlemen! The name of this town is not just Stonewall. No, sir! The name of this town is General Stonewall Jackson! That great general of the Confederate States of America! That great defender of the South! That great defender of the white man, and the rights of the white man! |

| | |
|---|---|
| *Spuddy*<br>*Ransom* | *(Coming out of his books)* He's right! For once, Catfish Giddy, you're right! Gentlemen, if you want to drive wickedness out of Black Ankle County, you'll join with me in the Black Ankle Branch of the Ku Klux Klan. If you want to drive the corn-whiskey distillers, the loose women, the gypsy mule traders, and the fortune tellers out of Black Ankle County, you'll join with us in the Invisible Empire. |
| *Catfish Giddy* | Yes, sir, gentlemen! Tomorrow, at four in the afternoon, we'll meet in the hall over the bank where we had the Chamber of Commerce meetings and the Boosters meetings. But this time it's going to be different! |
| *Spuddy*<br>*Ransom* | Be there! Join the crusade against evil! |
| *Announcer* | That's the way the Black Ankle County Branch of the Ku Klux Klan was born. Seventeen citizens of Stonewall showed up at that meeting, and in no time at all they had their white robes, the uniform of the Klan. Some even bought white robes for their mules. The boys and girls of Stonewall were curious about the Klan. They would hide in the tall grass, watching the Knights come and go in their battles against sin. |
| *Joe* | *(Hiding with the others)* What have you got there, Frankie? |
| *Frankie* | It's my father's Klan book. |
| *Joe* | What does it say? |

| | |
|---|---|
| Frankie | (*Reading*) The Ku Klux Klan stands on a platform of 100 percent Americanism, white supremacy in the South, deportation of aliens, purity of womanhood, and eradication of the chain store. |
| Willie | That's a lot of big words. What do you mean, eradication of the chain store? |
| Freddie | It means no more chain stores. |
| Willie | But we haven't got any chain stores around here. |
| Frankie | That's what it says, though. Listen to this! It costs ten dollars to join. |
| Robert | That's a lot of money! |
| Frankie | That's nothing! That robe and hood they wear costs sixty-five dollars! |
| Steve | Wow! I wonder if my mother knows that! She sure would holler! |
| Frankie | To fight against Catholics and Jews and Negroes and labor unions? That's what it says in the book. She wouldn't holler about that? |
| Robert | My Ma would holler about anything. She doesn't think much of this Klan anyway. She says the men joined up just to get away from their wives and kids after dinner. |
| Frankie | Maybe. Hush! Here they come! |
| Joe | Hey! Some of those mules have got robes and hoods, too! |
| Steve | Not all of them do. |

| | |
|---|---|
| *Joe* | Mules with white robes, mules without them. That's going to be trouble, if I know my mules! |
| *Steve* | Say! That's my Pa! |
| *Robert* | Where? |
| *Steve* | On the mule! The one without the bed sheet! Wow! That mule sure is scared. |
| *Joe* | Listen to them neigh! They're scared, all right! |
| *Frankie* | There they go! Look at those mules buck! |
| *Robert* | Someone just fell! |
| *Steve* | (*Beginning to get up out of the grass*) It's my Pa! |
| *Frankie* | Stay where you are! Do you want to get us into trouble? |
| *Steve* | But my Pa is hurt! |
| *Joe* | It's more than your Pa! Look at them all! Lying all over the place! And the mules are running like they've never run before! They'll never find *those* mules again! |
| *Announcer* | They got the mules back, but it wasn't easy, and Steve's Pa had three broken ribs and a broken leg. You couldn't blame it on the mules. They weren't as smart as Steve. Steve knew his father, whatever he was wearing, but a mule couldn't know that an animal in a white bed sheet was just another mule, in a white bed sheet. Anyway, that was the end of mule-riding for the Black Ankle Klansmen. Catfish Giddy, for one, wasn't sorry. He was really too fat for a mule, and he could do better in an automobile on the highways. |

**150**   *The Downfall of Fascism*

| | |
|---|---|
| *Catfish Giddy* | Gentlemen, we are ready for a report on the activities of the Black Ankle County Branch of the Ku Klux Klan. |
| *Henderson* | Last Tuesday night, we burned a cross in the yard of the Negro Methodist Church. |
| *Smith* | Last Wednesday night, we got the blacksmith. We tarred and feathered him, and threw him into the millpond. |
| *Spuddy Ransom* | And that's what he had coming to him for all the cursing he does. We've got to purify Stonewall. We've got to drive sin out of Black Ankle County. |
| *Waters* | Spuddy Ransom is right! We smashed that loud phonograph they have down in that cafe where all the colored people do their singing and dancing. |
| *Spuddy Ransom* | When they're not in church. |
| *Brown* | And don't forget the A & P store we wrecked. It isn't rightfully in Black Ankle County, but it's a warning to all them chain stores to keep out of here. |
| *Catfish Giddy* | Right! Right! Now how about that Jew who lives over his dry-goods store? |
| *Smith* | A lot of us owe him money. |
| *Spuddy Ransom* | But you know what our Ku Klux Klan book says about Jews! |

*The Downfall of Fascism* **151**

| | |
|---|---|
| Catfish Giddy | He sits up in his room over the dry-goods store, and all he does all night long is read. Foreign books, maybe. There's no telling what he's plotting. |
| Henderson | (Quietly) He's got a shotgun. |
| Spuddy Ransom | All the more reason to go after him! |
| Brown | I'm not sure about that. I don't want to get myself shot full of lead. (To Henderson) How do you know he's got a shotgun? |
| Henderson | I was in the General Store and saw him buy one. |
| Catfish Giddy | Maybe we ought to forget about him for a while. But keep an eye on him! |
| Brown | How about those whiskey distillers? They're no good! |
| Spuddy Ransom | You've got a point there, Brown! How about Sledge MacKellar? |
| Catfish Giddy | Well now, gentlemen, let's think this over. |
| Spuddy Ransom | Sledge MacKellar makes whiskey, and whiskey is evil. |
| Henderson | That's right, Ransom. But there's one thing you've forgotten. MacKellar is Catfish Giddy's bootlegger. |
| Brown | And he's got a shotgun. |

| | |
|---|---|
| Smith | MacKellar says he'll blow the head off any Bed Sheet who sticks his head past the front gate. |
| Henderson | You heard him say that? |
| Smith | He said it to my face. "I'm a Democrat," he said, "and I've got my rights." He waved his shotgun in my face and he said it was loaded. "And I'm just aching to pull the trigger," he said. He's a mean one. |
| Henderson | I guess we'd better forget about MacKellar! |
| Catfish Giddy | How about the Kidney boys? They've got a still for making whiskey. |
| Brown | Pat, Pinky and Francis drink half the stuff they make. They're always drunk. |
| Smith | Yeah! They're Irish. They're Catholics. And they're sinners. |
| Henderson | And maybe they haven't got a shotgun among them. |
| Spuddy Ransom | We'll break up their still. We'll throw the Kidney brothers out. That'll show the rest of them that we mean business. How about raiding them this Friday night? |
| Announcer | The date was set. The Klan would gather, go down as an army and drive the brothers and sin from Black Ankle County. Of course, the Kidney brothers got wind of the great plan, and they just didn't sit around waiting. Not in the beginning, anyway. |

*The Downfall of Fascism*  **153**

| | |
|---|---|
| *Francis* | Have you got everything ready? |
| *Pat* | All I've got to do is pull this switch and the dynamite will blow them all to heaven, or wherever else they're going. |
| *Pinky* | I've got my switch ready, too. How about you, Francis? |
| *Francis* | Ready. They've got three ways to get into this house, and a barrel of dynamite will blow those Bed Sheets to Kingdom Come, whichever way they try to get in. |
| *Uncle Bowleg* | That dynamite is going to make an awful lot of noise! |
| *Pat* | You bet it is! Put out the lights, Uncle Bowleg. I want to see all those bright colors the dynamite is going to make. |
| *Uncle Bowleg* | *(Putting out the lights)* It won't do much good, putting out the lights, I mean. Look at that big moon. |
| *Pinky* | What I want to see is the Bed Sheets. |
| *Francis* | *(Picking up a jug)* This jug is empty. Get us some whiskey, Uncle Bowleg. |
| *Uncle Bowleg* | Are you sure? You've emptied a couple of these jugs already. You don't want to get drunk, do you? |
| *Pinky* | *(Laughs)* Drunk? Who's sober? I can't wait for those Bed Sheets! |

**154** *The Downfall of Fascism*

| | |
|---|---|
| *Francis* | I'm finished waiting! I want to hear that dynamite go bang! I'm going to test mine! They won't be coming in through this side door anyway! |
| *Pat* | Francis! |
| *Announcer* | It was too late! There was a roar and a mighty explosion. It tore a huge pine tree and tossed it into the road, and it tossed half the people in Stonewall out of their beds. The old women were sure that Judgment Day had come at last. |
| *Pinky* | I think they're coming now, Pat! Throw your switch! Throw your switch! |
| *Announcer* | And there was another mighty explosion. In the excitement, Pinky pulled his switch, and the damage was complete. The slats fell out of all the beds, the kitchen stove fell apart, the whole porch was torn loose from the house. The chicken house blew up and all the chickens were killed — except the rooster, who never crowed again. It was a strange and awful sight that Catfish Giddy and Spuddy Ransom looked at the next morning. |
| *Catfish Giddy* | That sure is some hole, Spuddy, I'm glad I wasn't here last night, when they were digging it. |
| *Spuddy Ransom* | Somebody might have been murdered, Catfish. It's a good thing the Klan didn't ride last night. |
| *Catfish Giddy* | Friend, I've resigned. |
| *Spuddy Ransom* | Resigned from what? |

| | |
|---|---|
| *Catfish Giddy* | It doesn't make any difference what I've resigned from. I just want you to know I've resigned. |
| *Announcer* | And that was the end of the Black Ankle County Branch of the Ku Klux Klan. It never held another meeting. The wives ripped up their husbands' Klan robes and made a pillowcase out of each of them. Mrs. Catfish Giddy made two of them out of Catfish's robe. As a matter of fact, as she told her neighbors, Catfish was so fat that she found enough material in his robe to make two pillowcases, an apron and a tablecloth. Catfish sure was a fat man. |